2018 SQA Specimen and Past Papers with Answers

Higher
PHYSICS

2017 & 2018 Exams
and 2018 Specimen Question Paper

Hodder Gibson Study Skills Advice – Higher Physics	– page 3
Hodder Gibson Study Skills Advice – General	– page 5
2017 EXAM	– page 7
2018 EXAM	– page 65
2018 SPECIMEN QUESTION PAPER	– page 131
ANSWERS	– page 205

HODDER GIBSON
AN HACHETTE UK COMPANY

This book contains the official SQA 2017 and 2018 Exams, and the 2018 Specimen Question Paper for Higher Physics, with associated SQA-approved answers modified from the official marking instructions that accompany the paper.

In addition the book contains study skills advice. This advice has been specially commissioned by Hodder Gibson, and has been written by experienced senior teachers and examiners in line with the Higher syllabus and assessment outlines. This is not SQA material but has been devised to provide further guidance for Higher examinations.

Hodder Gibson is grateful to the copyright holders, as credited on the final page of the Answer section, for permission to use their material. Every effort has been made to trace the copyright holders and to obtain their permission for the use of copyright material. Hodder Gibson will be happy to receive information allowing us to rectify any error or omission in future editions.

Hachette UK's policy is to use papers that are natural, renewable and recyclable products and made from wood grown in sustainable forests. The logging and manufacturing processes are expected to conform to the environmental regulations of the country of origin.

Orders: please contact Bookpoint Ltd, 130 Park Drive, Milton Park, Abingdon, Oxon OX14 4SE. Telephone: (44) 01235 827827. Fax: (44) 01235 400454. Lines are open 9.00–5.00, Monday to Saturday, with a 24-hour message answering service. Visit our website at www.hoddereducation.co.uk. Hodder Gibson can also be contacted directly at hoddergibson@hodder.co.uk

This collection first published in 2018 by
Hodder Gibson, an imprint of Hodder Education,
An Hachette UK Company
211 St Vincent Street
Glasgow G2 5QY

Typeset by Aptara, Inc.

Printed in the UK

A catalogue record for this title is available from the British Library

ISBN: 978-1-5104-5716-4

2 1

2019 2018

Introduction

Higher Physics

Assessment

The Course Assessment falls into three categories:

Question Paper 1

There are 25 multiple choice questions - ensure you answer all of these, even if it means guessing an answer.

Time: 45 minutes

Question Paper 2

This section consists of restricted and extended-response questions. The majority of the marks will be awarded for applying **knowledge and understanding**. The other marks will be awarded for applying **scientific inquiry**, **scientific analytical thinking** and **problem-solving skills**.

The mark scored will be out of **130** and then scaled to be out of **95**.

Time: 2 hours 15 minutes

Assignment

The report will be submitted to SQA for external marking. This will be marked out of **20** and then scaled to be out of **30**.

Time: 8 hours, of which 2 hours is allowed for the report stage

Total course assessment mark: 150

The examination – general points

Standard 3-marker

Look out for these. The breakdown of the marks will be:

1 mark – selecting formula

1 mark – substitution

1 mark – answer, including unit.

Do not rearrange formulae in algebraic form. Select the appropriate formula, substitute the given values, and then rearrange the formula to obtain the required unknown. **This minimises the risk of wrong substitution.**

For example:

Calculate the acceleration of a mass of 5 kg when acted on by a resultant force of 10 N.

Solution 1	Solution 2	Solution 3
$F = ma$ (1)	$F = ma$ (1)	$F = ma$ (1)
$10 = 5a$ (1)	$a = m/F = 5/10$ (1)	$10 = 5a$ (1)
$a = 2 \text{ ms}^{-2}$ (1)	$= 0.5 \text{ ms}^{-2}$	$= 0.5 \text{ ms}^{-2}$
3 marks	**1 mark for selecting formula.**	**2 marks (1 mark for selecting formula 1 mark for correct substitution.)**

Use of the data sheet and data booklet

Clearly show where you have substituted a value from the data sheet. For example, do not leave H_0 in a formula. You must show the value of H_0 has been correctly substituted.

Rounding – do not round the given values.

E.g. mass of a proton $= 1.673 \times 10^{-27}$ kg
     NOT 1.67×10^{-27} kg.

Although many of the required formulae are given, **it is better to know the basic formulae to gain time in the examination**.

"Show" questions

Generally **all steps** for these must be given. **Do not assume that substitutions are obvious to the marker.** All formulae used must be stated separately and then clearly substituted if required. Many candidates will look at the end product and somehow end up with the required answer. The marker has to ensure that the path to the solution is clear. It is good practice to state why certain formulae are used, explaining the Physics behind them. Remember, at the end of the question, to give the final answer or required derived formula, even though they are given in the question. Ensure that you include the unit in the final answer, where required.

Definitions

Know and understand definitions given in the course. Definitions often come from the interpretation of a formulae.

For example, 1 Farad is equivalent to a 1CV^{-1} using $(C = Q/V)$.

Diagrams, graphs and sketch graphs

When drawing diagrams, use a ruler and appropriate labels. Angles will be important in certain diagrams. Too many candidates attempt to draw ray diagrams freehand.

When drawing graphs, use a ruler and pencil to draw the axes. Label the axes correctly including units and the origin.

When tackling sketch graphs, care should be taken to be as neat as possible. Ensure axes are drawn in pencil with a ruler. Also ensure you use a ruler to draw a straight line graph but do not force the line through the origin.

Significant figures

Do not round off in intermediate calculations, but round off in the final answer to an appropriate number of figures.

Rounding off to three significant figures in the final answer will generally be acceptable.

Prefixes

Ensure you know all the prefixes required and be able to convert them to the correct power of 10.

"Explain"/descriptive questions

These tend to be done poorly. Ensure all points are covered and read over again in order to check there are no mistakes.

Try to be clear and to the point, highlighting the relevant Physics.

Do not use up and down arrows in a description – this may help you in shorthand, but these must be translated to words.

Be aware some answers require justification. No attempt at a justification can mean no marks awarded.

Two or more attempts at an answer

The attempt that the candidate does not want to be considered should be scored out. Otherwise zero marks could be awarded.

Do not be tempted to give extra information that might be incorrect – marks could be deducted for each incorrect piece of information. This might include converting incorrectly m to nm in the last line of an answer, when it is not required.

At the end of the exam, if you have time, quickly go over each answer and make sure you have the correct unit inserted.

Skills

Experimental descriptions / planning

You could well be called on to describe an experimental set-up.

Ensure your description is clear enough for another person to repeat it.

Include a clearly labelled diagram.

Suggested improvements to experimental procedure

Look at the percentage uncertainties in the measured quantities and decide which is most significant. Suggest how the size of this uncertainty could be reduced – do not suggest "use better apparatus"! It might be better to repeat readings, so random uncertainty is reduced or increase distances to reduce the percentage uncertainty in scale reading. There could be a systematic uncertainty that is affecting all readings. It really depends on the experiment. Use your judgement.

Handling data

Relationships

There are two methods to prove a direct or inverse relationship.

Graphical approach

Plot the graphs with the appropriate x and y values and look for a straight line – better plotted in pencil in case of mistakes. **Do not force a line through the origin!** (A vs B for a direct relationship, C vs I / D for an inverse relationship)

Algebraic approach

If it appears that A ∝ B then calculate the value of A/B **for all values**.

If these show that A/B = k then the relationship holds.

If it appears that C ∝ 1/D then calculate the value C.D **for all values**.

If these show that C.D = k then the relationship holds.

Using the equation of a straight line, y = mx + c.

Be aware that the gradient of the line and the intercept can often lead to required values.

For example, finding the internal resistance and emf of a cell.

$E = IR + I r = V + I r$

$V = - r I + E$ in the form of $y = mx + c$

By plotting the graph of V against I, the value of the gradient will give − r and the intercept will give E.

Ensure you are clear on how to calculate the gradient of a line.

Unfamiliar content

If you come across unfamiliar content such as an equation or measurements from an unfamiliar experiment – don't panic! Just read the instructions and apply the skills gained from the course. Relationships between the quantities can be found graphically or algebraically.

Uncertainties

In this section you need to understand the following:

Systematic, scale reading (analogue and digital) and random uncertainties.

Percentage and absolute uncertainties.

Percentage uncertainty in final answer is taken as the largest percentage uncertainty in the components.

E.g. V = (7.5 ± 0.1) V	I = (0.85 ± 0.05) A
= 7.5V ± 1.3%	= 0.85 A ± 5.8%
R = V / I = 7.5 / 0.85 = 8.8 Ω + 5.8% = (8.8 ± 0.1) Ω	

Open-ended questions

There will generally be two open-ended questions in the paper worth 3 marks each. Some candidates look upon these as mini essays. Remember that they are only worth 3 marks and it gives the opportunity to demonstrate knowledge and understanding. **However, do not spend too long on these. It might be better to revisit them at the end of the exam.**

Some students prefer to use bullet points to highlight the main areas of understanding.

Ensure you reread the question and understand exactly what is being asked.

Once you have written your response, read over it again to ensure it makes sense.

Good luck!

Remember that the rewards for passing Higher Physics are well worth it! Your pass will help you get the future you want for yourself. In the exam, be confident in your own ability. If you're not sure how to answer a question, trust your instincts and just give it a go anyway – keep calm and don't panic! GOOD LUCK!

Study Skills – what you need to know to pass exams!

General exam revision: 20 top tips

When preparing for exams, it is easy to feel unsure of where to start or how to revise. This guide to general exam revision provides a good starting place, and, as these are very general tips, they can be applied to all your exams.

1. Start revising in good time.

Don't leave revision until the last minute – this will make you panic and it will be difficult to learn. Make a revision timetable that counts down the weeks to go.

2. Work to a study plan.

Set up sessions of work spread through the weeks ahead. Make sure each session has a focus and a clear purpose. What will you study, when and why? Be realistic about what you can achieve in each session, and don't be afraid to adjust your plans as needed.

3. Make sure you know exactly when your exams are.

Get your exam dates from the SQA website and use the timetable builder tool to create your own exam schedule. You will also get a personalised timetable from your school, but this might not be until close to the exam period.

4. Make sure that you know the topics that make up each course.

Studying is easier if material is in manageable chunks – why not use the SQA topic headings or create your own from your class notes? Ask your teacher for help on this if you are not sure.

5. Break the chunks up into even smaller bits.

The small chunks should be easier to cope with. Remember that they fit together to make larger ideas. Even the process of chunking down will help!

6. Ask yourself these key questions for each course:

- Are all topics compulsory or are there choices?
- Which topics seem to come up time and time again?
- Which topics are your strongest and which are your weakest?

Use your answers to these questions to work out how much time you will need to spend revising each topic.

7. Make sure you know what to expect in the exam.

The subject-specific introduction to this book will help with this. Make sure you can answer these questions:

- How is the paper structured?
- How much time is there for each part of the exam?
- What types of question are involved? These will vary depending on the subject so read the subject-specific section carefully.

8. Past papers are a vital revision tool!

Use past papers to support your revision wherever possible. This book contains the answers and mark schemes too – refer to these carefully when checking your work. Using the mark scheme is useful; even if you don't manage to get all the marks available first time when you first practise, it helps you identify how to extend and develop your answers to get more marks next time – and of course, in the real exam.

9. Use study methods that work well for you.

People study and learn in different ways. Reading and looking at diagrams suits some students. Others prefer to listen and hear material – what about reading out loud or getting a friend or family member to do this for you? You could also record and play back material.

10. There are three tried and tested ways to make material stick in your long-term memory:

- Practising – e.g. rehearsal, repeating
- Organising – e.g. making drawings, lists, diagrams, tables, memory aids
- Elaborating – e.g. incorporating the material into a story or an imagined journey

11. Learn actively.

Most people prefer to learn actively – for example, making notes, highlighting, redrawing and redrafting, making up memory aids, or writing past paper answers. A good way to stay engaged and inspired is to mix and match these methods – find the combination that best suits you. This is likely to vary depending on the topic or subject.

12. Be an expert.

Be sure to have a few areas in which you feel you are an expert. This often works because at least some of them will come up, which can boost confidence.

13. Try some visual methods.

Use symbols, diagrams, charts, flashcards, post-it notes etc. Don't forget – the brain takes in chunked images more easily than loads of text.

14. Remember – practice makes perfect.

Work on difficult areas again and again. Look and read – then test yourself. You cannot do this too much.

15. Try past papers against the clock.

Practise writing answers in a set time. This is a good habit from the start but is especially important when you get closer to exam time.

16. Collaborate with friends.

Test each other and talk about the material – this can really help. Two brains are better than one! It is amazing how talking about a problem can help you solve it.

17. Know your weaknesses.

Ask your teacher for help to identify what you don't know. Try to do this as early as possible. If you are having trouble, it is probably with a difficult topic, so your teacher will already be aware of this – most students will find it tough.

18. Have your materials organised and ready.

Know what is needed for each exam:

- Do you need a calculator or a ruler?
- Should you have pencils as well as pens?
- Will you need water or paper tissues?

19. Make full use of school resources.

Find out what support is on offer:

- Are there study classes available?
- When is the library open?
- When is the best time to ask for extra help?
- Can you borrow textbooks, study guides, past papers, etc.?
- Is school open for Easter revision?

20. Keep fit and healthy!

Try to stick to a routine as much as possible, including with sleep. If you are tired, sluggish or dehydrated, it is difficult to see how concentration is even possible. Combine study with relaxation, drink plenty of water, eat sensibly, and get fresh air and exercise – all these things will help more than you could imagine. Good luck!

HIGHER

2017

National Qualifications 2017

X757/76/02

Physics
Section 1 — Questions

WEDNESDAY, 17 MAY
9:00 AM – 11:30 AM

Instructions for the completion of Section 1 are given on *Page two* of your question and answer booklet X757/76/01.

Record your answers on the answer grid on *Page three* of your question and answer booklet.

Reference may be made to the Data Sheet on *Page two* of this booklet and to the Relationships Sheet X757/76/11.

Before leaving the examination room you must give your question and answer booklet to the Invigilator; if you do not, you may lose all the marks for this paper.

DATA SHEET

COMMON PHYSICAL QUANTITIES

Quantity	Symbol	Value	Quantity	Symbol	Value
Speed of light in vacuum	c	$3.00 \times 10^8 \, m\,s^{-1}$	Planck's constant	h	$6.63 \times 10^{-34} \, J\,s$
Magnitude of the charge on an electron	e	$1.60 \times 10^{-19} \, C$	Mass of electron	m_e	$9.11 \times 10^{-31} \, kg$
Universal Constant of Gravitation	G	$6.67 \times 10^{-11} \, m^3\,kg^{-1}\,s^{-2}$	Mass of neutron	m_n	$1.675 \times 10^{-27} \, kg$
Gravitational acceleration on Earth	g	$9.8 \, m\,s^{-2}$	Mass of proton	m_p	$1.673 \times 10^{-27} \, kg$
Hubble's constant	H_0	$2.3 \times 10^{-18} \, s^{-1}$			

REFRACTIVE INDICES

The refractive indices refer to sodium light of wavelength 589 nm and to substances at a temperature of 273 K.

Substance	Refractive index	Substance	Refractive index
Diamond	2·42	Water	1·33
Crown glass	1·50	Air	1·00

SPECTRAL LINES

Element	Wavelength/nm	Colour	Element	Wavelength/nm	Colour
Hydrogen	656	Red	Cadmium	644	Red
	486	Blue-green		509	Green
	434	Blue-violet		480	Blue
	410	Violet		Lasers	
	397	Ultraviolet	Element	Wavelength/nm	Colour
	389	Ultraviolet	Carbon dioxide	9550 }10590	Infrared
Sodium	589	Yellow	Helium-neon	633	Red

PROPERTIES OF SELECTED MATERIALS

Substance	Density/kg m^{-3}	Melting Point/K	Boiling Point/K
Aluminium	2.70×10^3	933	2623
Copper	8.96×10^3	1357	2853
Ice	9.20×10^2	273	. . . .
Sea Water	1.02×10^3	264	377
Water	1.00×10^3	273	373
Air	1·29	. . . .	. . . .
Hydrogen	9.0×10^{-2}	14	20

The gas densities refer to a temperature of 273 K and a pressure of 1.01×10^5 Pa.

SECTION 1 — 20 marks

Attempt ALL questions

1. The graph shows how the velocity of an object varies with time.

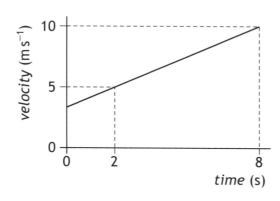

The acceleration of the object is

A $0.83\,\text{m s}^{-2}$

B $1.2\,\text{m s}^{-2}$

C $2.5\,\text{m s}^{-2}$

D $5.0\,\text{m s}^{-2}$

E $6.0\,\text{m s}^{-2}$.

2. A block is resting on a horizontal surface.

A force of 24 N is now applied as shown and the block slides along the surface.

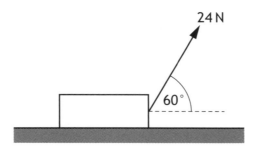

24 N

60°

The mass of the block is 20 kg.

The acceleration of the block is $0.20\,\text{m s}^{-2}$.

The force of friction acting on the block is

A   4·0 N

B   8·0 N

C   12 N

D   16 N

E   25 N.

3. The graph shows how the vertical speed of a skydiver varies with time.

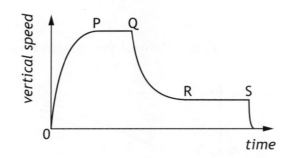

A student uses information from the graph to make the following statements.

I   The acceleration of the skydiver is greatest between P and Q.

II The air resistance acting on the skydiver between Q and R is less than the weight of the skydiver.

III The forces acting on the skydiver are balanced between R and S.

Which of these statements is/are correct?

A   I only

B   II only

C   III only

D   I and II only

E   I , II and III

4. A spacecraft is travelling at a constant speed of $2 \cdot 75 \times 10^8\,\mathrm{m\,s^{-1}}$ relative to a planet.

A technician on the spacecraft measures the length of the spacecraft as 125 m.

An observer on the planet measures the length of the spacecraft as

A   36 m

B   50 m

C   124 m

D   314 m

E   433 m.

5. A galaxy has a recessional velocity of $0\cdot30c$.

Hubble's Law predicts that the distance between Earth and this galaxy is

A $1\cdot3 \times 10^{17}\,\text{m}$

B $3\cdot9 \times 10^{25}\,\text{m}$

C $1\cdot3 \times 10^{26}\,\text{m}$

D $1\cdot4 \times 10^{41}\,\text{m}$

E $4\cdot5 \times 10^{42}\,\text{m}$.

6. Measurements of the expansion rate of the Universe lead to the conclusion that the rate of expansion is increasing.

Present theory proposes that this is due to

A   redshift

B   dark matter

C   dark energy

D   the gravitational force

E   cosmic microwave background radiation.

7. A student makes the following statements about the radiation emitted by stellar objects.

I   Stellar objects emit radiation over a wide range of frequencies.

II   The peak wavelength of radiation is longer for hotter objects than for cooler objects.

III   At all frequencies, hotter objects emit more radiation per unit surface area per unit time than cooler objects.

Which of these statements is/are correct?

A   I only

B   III only

C   I and II only

D   I and III only

E   I, II and III

[Turn over

8. The following statement represents a nuclear reaction.

$$^{256}_{103}\text{Lr} \rightarrow Z + {}^{4}_{2}\text{He}$$

Nucleus Z is

A $^{252}_{101}\text{Md}$

B $^{252}_{101}\text{No}$

C $^{256}_{101}\text{Md}$

D $^{260}_{105}\text{Db}$

E $^{252}_{103}\text{Lr}$.

9. Radiation is incident on a clean zinc plate causing photoelectrons to be emitted.

The source of radiation is replaced with one emitting radiation of a higher frequency.

The irradiance of the radiation incident on the plate remains unchanged.

Which row in the table shows the effect of this change on the maximum kinetic energy of a photoelectron and the number of photoelectrons emitted per second?

	Maximum kinetic energy of a photoelectron	Number of photoelectrons emitted per second
A	no change	no change
B	no change	increases
C	increases	no change
D	increases	decreases
E	decreases	increases

10. Ultraviolet radiation of frequency $7 \cdot 70 \times 10^{14}$ Hz is incident on the surface of a metal.

    Photoelectrons are emitted from the surface of the metal.

    The maximum kinetic energy of an emitted photoelectron is $2 \cdot 67 \times 10^{-19}$ J.

    The work function of the metal is

    A $1 \cdot 07 \times 10^{-19}$ J

    B $2 \cdot 44 \times 10^{-19}$ J

    C $2 \cdot 67 \times 10^{-19}$ J

    D $5 \cdot 11 \times 10^{-19}$ J

    E $7 \cdot 78 \times 10^{-19}$ J.

11. A student makes the following statements about waves from coherent sources.

    I   Waves from coherent sources have the same velocity.

    II   Waves from coherent sources have the same wavelength.

    III Waves from coherent sources have a constant phase relationship.

    Which of these statements is/are correct?

    A   I only

    B   II only

    C   I and II only

    D   I and III only

    E   I, II and III

[Turn over

12. A ray of red light passes from a liquid to a transparent solid.

The solid and the liquid have the same refractive index for this light.

Which row in the table shows what happens to the speed and wavelength of the light as it passes from the liquid into the solid?

	Speed	Wavelength
A	decreases	decreases
B	decreases	increases
C	no change	increases
D	increases	no change
E	no change	no change

13. A ray of blue light passes from air into a transparent block as shown.

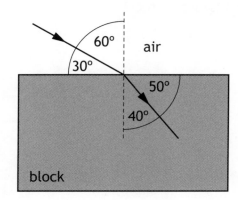

The speed of this light in the block is

A $1{\cdot}80 \times 10^8\,\text{m s}^{-1}$

B $1{\cdot}96 \times 10^8\,\text{m s}^{-1}$

C $2{\cdot}00 \times 10^8\,\text{m s}^{-1}$

D $2{\cdot}23 \times 10^8\,\text{m s}^{-1}$

E $2{\cdot}65 \times 10^8\,\text{m s}^{-1}$.

14. A student carries out an experiment to investigate how irradiance varies with distance.

A small lamp is placed at a distance d away from a light meter. The irradiance I at this distance is displayed on the meter. This measurement is repeated for a range of different distances.

The student uses these results to produce the graph shown.

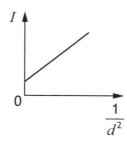

The graph indicates that there is a systematic uncertainty in this experiment.

Which of the following would be most likely to reduce the systematic uncertainty in this experiment?

A   Repeating the readings and calculating mean values.

B   Replacing the small lamp with a larger lamp.

C   Decreasing the brightness of the lamp.

D   Repeating the experiment in a darkened room.

E   Increasing the range of distances.

15. A point source of light is 8·00 m away from a surface. The irradiance, due to the point source, at the surface is 50·0 mW m^{-2}. The point source is now moved to a distance of 12·0 m from the surface.

The irradiance, due to the point source, at the surface is now

A   22·2 mW m^{-2}

B   26·0 mW m^{-2}

C   33·3 mW m^{-2}

D   75·0 mW m^{-2}

E   267 mW m^{-2}.

[Turn over

16. The output from an a.c. power supply is connected to an oscilloscope. The trace seen on the oscilloscope screen is shown.

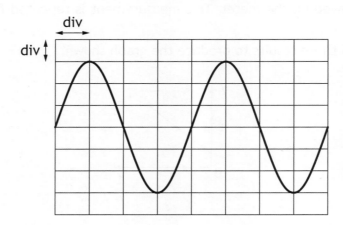

The Y-gain setting on the oscilloscope is 1·0 V/div.

The r.m.s. voltage of the power supply is

A   2·1 V

B   3·0 V

C   4·0 V

D   4·2 V

E   6·0 V.

17. A 20 µF capacitor is connected to a 12 V d.c. supply.

The maximum charge stored on the capacitor is

A $1·4 \times 10^{-3}$ C

B $2·4 \times 10^{-4}$ C

C $1·4 \times 10^{-4}$ C

D $1·7 \times 10^{-6}$ C

E $6·0 \times 10^{-7}$ C.

18. A circuit containing a capacitor is set up as shown.

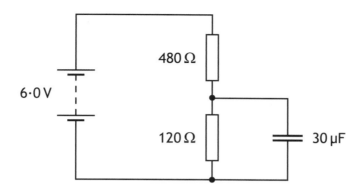

The supply has negligible internal resistance.

The maximum energy stored in the capacitor is

A $5 \cdot 4 \times 10^{-4}$ J

B $3 \cdot 5 \times 10^{-4}$ J

C $1 \cdot 4 \times 10^{-4}$ J

D $3 \cdot 4 \times 10^{-5}$ J

E $2 \cdot 2 \times 10^{-5}$ J.

19. A student makes the following statements about conductors, insulators and semiconductors.

I   In conductors, the conduction band is completely filled with electrons.

II   In insulators, the gap between the valence band and the conduction band is large.

III   In semiconductors, increasing the temperature increases the conductivity.

Which of these statements is/are correct?

A   I only

B   II only

C   III only

D   I and II only

E   II and III only

[Turn over for next question

20. Astronomers use the following relationship to determine the distance, d, to a star.

$$F = \frac{L}{4\pi d^2}$$

For a particular star the following measurements are recorded:

apparent brightness, $F = 4\cdot4 \times 10^{-10}\,\mathrm{W\,m^{-2}}$

luminosity, $L = 6\cdot1 \times 10^{30}\,\mathrm{W}$

Based on this information, the distance to this star is

A $3\cdot3 \times 10^{19}\,\mathrm{m}$

B $1\cdot5 \times 10^{21}\,\mathrm{m}$

C $3\cdot7 \times 10^{36}\,\mathrm{m}$

D $1\cdot1 \times 10^{39}\,\mathrm{m}$

E $3\cdot9 \times 10^{39}\,\mathrm{m}.$

[END OF SECTION 1. NOW ATTEMPT THE QUESTIONS IN SECTION 2 OF YOUR QUESTION AND ANSWER BOOKLET]

National Qualifications 2017

X757/76/11

Physics
Relationship Sheet

WEDNESDAY, 17 MAY
9:00 AM – 11:30 AM

Relationships required for Physics Higher

$d = \bar{v}t$

$s = \bar{v}t$

$v = u + at$

$s = ut + \frac{1}{2}at^2$

$v^2 = u^2 + 2as$

$s = \frac{1}{2}(u + v)t$

$W = mg$

$F = ma$

$E_W = Fd$

$E_p = mgh$

$E_k = \frac{1}{2}mv^2$

$P = \dfrac{E}{t}$

$p = mv$

$Ft = mv - mu$

$F = G\dfrac{m_1 m_2}{r^2}$

$t' = \dfrac{t}{\sqrt{1 - \left(\frac{v}{c}\right)^2}}$

$l' = l\sqrt{1 - \left(\frac{v}{c}\right)^2}$

$f_o = f_s\left(\dfrac{v}{v \pm v_s}\right)$

$z = \dfrac{\lambda_{observed} - \lambda_{rest}}{\lambda_{rest}}$

$z = \dfrac{v}{c}$

$v = H_0 d$

$W = QV$

$E = mc^2$

$E = hf$

$E_k = hf - hf_0$

$E_2 - E_1 = hf$

$T = \dfrac{1}{f}$

$v = f\lambda$

$d\sin\theta = m\lambda$

$n = \dfrac{\sin\theta_1}{\sin\theta_2}$

$\dfrac{\sin\theta_1}{\sin\theta_2} = \dfrac{\lambda_1}{\lambda_2} = \dfrac{v_1}{v_2}$

$\sin\theta_c = \dfrac{1}{n}$

$I = \dfrac{k}{d^2}$

$I = \dfrac{P}{A}$

path difference $= m\lambda$ or $\left(m + \frac{1}{2}\right)\lambda$ where $m = 0, 1, 2 \ldots$

random uncertainty $= \dfrac{\text{max. value} - \text{min. value}}{\text{number of values}}$

$V_{peak} = \sqrt{2}V_{rms}$

$I_{peak} = \sqrt{2}I_{rms}$

$Q = It$

$V = IR$

$P = IV = I^2 R = \dfrac{V^2}{R}$

$R_T = R_1 + R_2 + \ldots$

$\dfrac{1}{R_T} = \dfrac{1}{R_1} + \dfrac{1}{R_2} + \ldots$

$E = V + Ir$

$V_1 = \left(\dfrac{R_1}{R_1 + R_2}\right)V_s$

$\dfrac{V_1}{V_2} = \dfrac{R_1}{R_2}$

$C = \dfrac{Q}{V}$

$E = \frac{1}{2}QV = \frac{1}{2}CV^2 = \frac{1}{2}\dfrac{Q^2}{C}$

Additional Relationships

Circle

circumference $= 2\pi r$

area $= \pi r^2$

Sphere

area $= 4\pi r^2$

volume $= \frac{4}{3}\pi r^3$

Trigonometry

$\sin\Theta = \dfrac{\text{opposite}}{\text{hypotenuse}}$

$\cos\Theta = \dfrac{\text{adjacent}}{\text{hypotenuse}}$

$\tan\Theta = \dfrac{\text{opposite}}{\text{adjacent}}$

$\sin^2\Theta + \cos^2\Theta = 1$

Electron Arrangements of Elements

Key

| Atomic number |
| Symbol |
| Electron arrangement |
| Name |

Transition Elements

Group 1 (1) / Group 2 (2)

Group 1 (1)	Group 2 (2)
1 **H** Hydrogen	
3 **Li** 2,1 Lithium	4 **Be** 2,2 Beryllium
11 **Na** 2,8,1 Sodium	12 **Mg** 2,8,2 Magnesium
19 **K** 2,8,8,1 Potassium	20 **Ca** 2,8,8,2 Calcium
37 **Rb** 2,8,18,8,1 Rubidium	38 **Sr** 2,8,18,8,2 Strontium
55 **Cs** 2,8,18,18,8,1 Caesium	56 **Ba** 2,8,18,18,8,2 Barium
87 **Fr** 2,8,18,32,18,8,1 Francium	88 **Ra** 2,8,18,32,18,8,2 Radium

Transition Elements

(3)	(4)	(5)	(6)	(7)	(8)	(9)	(10)	(11)	(12)
21 **Sc** 2,8,9,2 Scandium	22 **Ti** 2,8,10,2 Titanium	23 **V** 2,8,11,2 Vanadium	24 **Cr** 2,8,13,1 Chromium	25 **Mn** 2,8,13,2 Manganese	26 **Fe** 2,8,14,2 Iron	27 **Co** 2,8,15,2 Cobalt	28 **Ni** 2,8,16,2 Nickel	29 **Cu** 2,8,18,1 Copper	30 **Zn** 2,8,18,2 Zinc
39 **Y** 2,8,18,9,2 Yttrium	40 **Zr** 2,8,18,10,2 Zirconium	41 **Nb** 2,8,18,12,1 Niobium	42 **Mo** 2,8,18,13,1 Molybdenum	43 **Tc** 2,8,18,13,2 Technetium	44 **Ru** 2,8,18,15,1 Ruthenium	45 **Rh** 2,8,18,16,1 Rhodium	46 **Pd** 2,8,18,18,0 Palladium	47 **Ag** 2,8,18,18,1 Silver	48 **Cd** 2,8,18,18,2 Cadmium
57 **La** 2,8,18,18,9,2 Lanthanum	72 **Hf** 2,8,18,32,10,2 Hafnium	73 **Ta** 2,8,18,32,11,2 Tantalum	74 **W** 2,8,18,32,12,2 Tungsten	75 **Re** 2,8,18,32,13,2 Rhenium	76 **Os** 2,8,18,32,14,2 Osmium	77 **Ir** 2,8,18,32,15,2 Iridium	78 **Pt** 2,8,18,32,17,1 Platinum	79 **Au** 2,8,18,32,18,1 Gold	80 **Hg** 2,8,18,32,18,2 Mercury
89 **Ac** 2,8,18,32,18,9,2 Actinium	104 **Rf** 2,8,18,32,32,10,2 Rutherfordium	105 **Db** 2,8,18,32,32,11,2 Dubnium	106 **Sg** 2,8,18,32,32,12,2 Seaborgium	107 **Bh** 2,8,18,32,32,13,2 Bohrium	108 **Hs** 2,8,18,32,32,14,2 Hassium	109 **Mt** 2,8,18,32,32,15,2 Meitnerium	110 **Ds** 2,8,18,32,32,17,1 Darmstadtium	111 **Rg** 2,8,18,32,32,18,1 Roentgenium	112 **Cn** 2,8,18,32,32,18,2 Copernicium

Groups 3–0

Group 3 (13)	Group 4 (14)	Group 5 (15)	Group 6 (16)	Group 7 (17)	Group 0 (18)
					2 **He** 2 Helium
5 **B** 2,3 Boron	6 **C** 2,4 Carbon	7 **N** 2,5 Nitrogen	8 **O** 2,6 Oxygen	9 **F** 2,7 Fluorine	10 **Ne** 2,8 Neon
13 **Al** 2,8,3 Aluminium	14 **Si** 2,8,4 Silicon	15 **P** 2,8,5 Phosphorus	16 **S** 2,8,6 Sulfur	17 **Cl** 2,8,7 Chlorine	18 **Ar** 2,8,8 Argon
31 **Ga** 2,8,18,3 Gallium	32 **Ge** 2,8,18,4 Germanium	33 **As** 2,8,18,5 Arsenic	34 **Se** 2,8,18,6 Selenium	35 **Br** 2,8,18,7 Bromine	36 **Kr** 2,8,18,8 Krypton
49 **In** 2,8,18,18,3 Indium	50 **Sn** 2,8,18,18,4 Tin	51 **Sb** 2,8,18,18,5 Antimony	52 **Te** 2,8,18,18,6 Tellurium	53 **I** 2,8,18,18,7 Iodine	54 **Xe** 2,8,18,18,8 Xenon
81 **Tl** 2,8,18,32,18,3 Thallium	82 **Pb** 2,8,18,32,18,4 Lead	83 **Bi** 2,8,18,32,18,5 Bismuth	84 **Po** 2,8,18,32,18,6 Polonium	85 **At** 2,8,18,32,18,7 Astatine	86 **Rn** 2,8,18,32,18,8 Radon

Lanthanides

No.	Symbol	Electron arrangement	Name
57	**La**	2,8,18,18,9,2	Lanthanum
58	**Ce**	2,8,18,20,8,2	Cerium
59	**Pr**	2,8,18,21,8,2	Praseodymium
60	**Nd**	2,8,18,22,8,2	Neodymium
61	**Pm**	2,8,18,23,8,2	Promethium
62	**Sm**	2,8,18,24,8,2	Samarium
63	**Eu**	2,8,18,25,8,2	Europium
64	**Gd**	2,8,18,25,9,2	Gadolinium
65	**Tb**	2,8,18,27,8,2	Terbium
66	**Dy**	2,8,18,28,8,2	Dysprosium
67	**Ho**	2,8,18,29,8,2	Holmium
68	**Er**	2,8,18,30,8,2	Erbium
69	**Tm**	2,8,18,31,8,2	Thulium
70	**Yb**	2,8,18,32,8,2	Ytterbium
71	**Lu**	2,8,18,32,9,2	Lutetium

Actinides

No.	Symbol	Electron arrangement	Name
89	**Ac**	2,8,18,32,18,9,2	Actinium
90	**Th**	2,8,18,32,18,10,2	Thorium
91	**Pa**	2,8,18,32,20,9,2	Protactinium
92	**U**	2,8,18,32,21,9,2	Uranium
93	**Np**	2,8,18,32,22,9,2	Neptunium
94	**Pu**	2,8,18,32,24,8,2	Plutonium
95	**Am**	2,8,18,32,25,8,2	Americium
96	**Cm**	2,8,18,32,25,9,2	Curium
97	**Bk**	2,8,18,32,27,8,2	Berkelium
98	**Cf**	2,8,18,32,28,8,2	Californium
99	**Es**	2,8,18,32,29,8,2	Einsteinium
100	**Fm**	2,8,18,32,30,8,2	Fermium
101	**Md**	2,8,18,32,31,8,2	Mendelevium
102	**No**	2,8,18,32,32,8,2	Nobelium
103	**Lr**	2,8,18,32,32,9,2	Lawrencium

FOR OFFICIAL USE

National
Qualifications
2017

Mark

X757/76/01

Physics
Section 1 — Answer Grid
and Section 2

WEDNESDAY, 17 MAY

9:00 AM – 11:30 AM

Fill in these boxes and read what is printed below.

Full name of centre

Town

Forename(s)

Surname

Number of seat

Date of birth

Day	Month	Year

Scottish candidate number

Total marks — 130

SECTION 1 — 20 marks
Attempt ALL questions.
Instructions for the completion of Section 1 are given on *Page two*.

SECTION 2 — 110 marks
Attempt ALL questions.

Reference may be made to the Data Sheet on *Page two* of the question paper X757/76/02 and to the Relationship Sheet X757/76/11.

Care should be taken to give an appropriate number of significant figures in the final answers to calculations.

Write your answers clearly in the spaces provided in this booklet. Additional space for answers and rough work is provided at the end of this booklet. If you use this space you must clearly identify the question number you are attempting. Any rough work must be written in this booklet. You should score through your rough work when you have written your final copy.

Use **blue** or **black** ink.

Before leaving the examination room you must give this booklet to the Invigilator; if you do not, you may lose all the marks for this paper.

SECTION 1 — 20 marks

The questions for Section 1 are contained in the question paper X757/76/02.

Read these and record your answers on the answer grid on *Page three* opposite.

Use **blue** or **black** ink. Do NOT use gel pens or pencil.

1. The answer to each question is **either** A, B, C, D or E. Decide what your answer is, then fill in the appropriate bubble (see sample question below).

2. There is **only one correct** answer to each question.

3. Any rough work must be written in the additional space for answers and rough work at the end of this booklet.

Sample Question

The energy unit measured by the electricity meter in your home is the:

    A   ampere

    B   kilowatt-hour

    C   watt

    D   coulomb

    E   volt.

The correct answer is **B** — kilowatt-hour. The answer **B** bubble has been clearly filled in (see below).

A	B	C	D	E
○	●	○	○	○

Changing an answer

If you decide to change your answer, cancel your first answer by putting a cross through it (see below) and fill in the answer you want. The answer below has been changed to **D**.

A	B	C	D	E
○	⊗	○	●	○

If you then decide to change back to an answer you have already scored out, put a tick (✓) to the **right** of the answer you want, as shown below:

A	B	C	D	E		A	B	C	D	E
○	⊗✓	○	⊗	○	or	○	⊗✓	○	○	○

SECTION 1 — Answer Grid

	A	B	C	D	E
1	○	○	○	○	○
2	○	○	○	○	○
3	○	○	○	○	○
4	○	○	○	○	○
5	○	○	○	○	○
6	○	○	○	○	○
7	○	○	○	○	○
8	○	○	○	○	○
9	○	○	○	○	○
10	○	○	○	○	○
11	○	○	○	○	○
12	○	○	○	○	○
13	○	○	○	○	○
14	○	○	○	○	○
15	○	○	○	○	○
16	○	○	○	○	○
17	○	○	○	○	○
18	○	○	○	○	○
19	○	○	○	○	○
20	○	○	○	○	○

[BLANK PAGE]

DO NOT WRITE ON THIS PAGE

[Turn over for SECTION 2

DO NOT WRITE ON THIS PAGE

MARKS | DO NOT WRITE IN THIS MARGIN

SECTION 2 — 110 marks
Attempt ALL questions

1. A student is on a stationary train.

    The train now accelerates along a straight level track.

    The student uses an app on a phone to measure the acceleration of the train.

    (a) The train accelerates uniformly at $0.32 \, \text{m s}^{-2}$ for 25 seconds.

         (i) State what is meant by *an acceleration of $0.32 \, \text{m s}^{-2}$*.   1

         (ii) Calculate the distance travelled by the train in the 25 seconds.   3
              Space for working and answer

MARKS | DO NOT WRITE IN THIS MARGIN

1. (continued)

(b) Later in the journey, the train is travelling at a constant speed as it approaches a bridge.

A horn on the train emits sound of frequency 270 Hz.

The frequency of the sound heard by a person standing on the bridge is 290 Hz.

The speed of sound in air is $340\,m\,s^{-1}$.

(i) Calculate the speed of the train.   **3**

Space for working and answer

(ii) The train continues to sound its horn as it passes under the bridge.

Explain why the frequency of the sound heard by the person standing on the bridge decreases as the train passes under the bridge and then moves away.

You may wish to use a diagram.   **1**

MARKS | DO NOT WRITE IN THIS MARGIN

2. A white snooker ball and a black snooker ball travel towards each other in a straight line.

The white ball and the black ball each have a mass of 0·180 kg.

Just before the balls collide head-on, the white ball is travelling at 2·60 m s⁻¹ to the right and the black ball is travelling at 1·80 m s⁻¹ to the left.

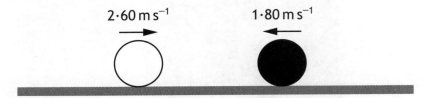

After the collision, the black ball rebounds with a velocity of 2·38 m s⁻¹ to the right.

(a) (i) Determine the velocity of the white ball immediately after the collision.   **3**

Space for working and answer

(ii) The collision between the balls is inelastic.

State what is meant by an *inelastic collision*.   **1**

MARKS | DO NOT WRITE IN THIS MARGIN

2. (continued)

(b) A student carries out an experiment to measure the average force exerted by a cue on a ball.

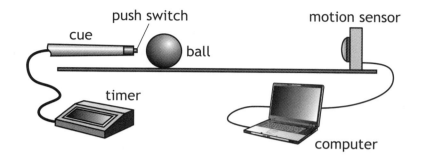

The cue hits the stationary ball.

The timer records the time the cue is in contact with the ball.

The computer displays the speed of the ball.

The results are shown.

Time of contact between the cue and the ball $= (0{\cdot}040 \pm 0{\cdot}001)\,\text{s}$

Speed of the ball immediately after contact $= (0{\cdot}84 \pm 0{\cdot}01)\,\text{m s}^{-1}$

Mass of the ball $= (0{\cdot}180 \pm 0{\cdot}001)\,\text{kg}$

(i) Calculate the average force exerted on the ball by the cue. An uncertainty in this value is not required.   **3**

Space for working and answer

(ii) Determine the percentage uncertainty in the value for the average force on the ball.   **2**

Space for working and answer

3. A ball is thrown vertically upwards.

The ball is above the ground when released.

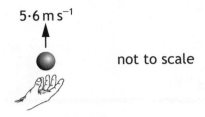

not to scale

ground

The graph shows how the vertical velocity of the ball varies with time from the instant it is released until just before it hits the ground.

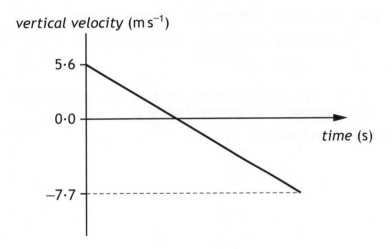

The effects of air resistance can be ignored.

(a)   (i)   Calculate the time taken for the ball to reach its maximum height.   3

Space for working and answer

MARKS | DO NOT WRITE IN THIS MARGIN

3. (a) (continued)

   (ii) Calculate the distance the ball falls from its maximum height to the ground.

   Space for working and answer

3

   (b) The ball is now thrown vertically upwards from the same height with a greater initial vertical velocity.

   Add a line to the graph below to show how the vertical velocity of the ball varies with time from the instant it is released until just before it hits the ground.

   The effects of air resistance can be ignored.

   Additional numerical values on the axes are not required.

3

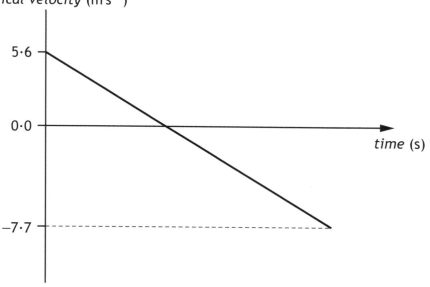

(An additional graph, if required, can be found on *Page thirty-nine*.)

[Turn over

4. Some motorways have variable speed limits, with overhead information boards displaying the maximum speed allowed. This system is designed to keep the traffic flowing and to avoid congestion.

Editorial Credit: Flik47 / Shutterstock.com

In this system, the flow of traffic is observed and the maximum speed to be displayed is determined using

$$speed = frequency \times wavelength$$

Use your knowledge of physics to comment on this system for determining the maximum speed to be displayed.

3

4.　(continued)

[Turn over

MARKS | DO NOT WRITE IN THIS MARGIN

5. Planets outside our solar system are called exoplanets.

An exoplanet of mass 5.69×10^{27} kg orbits a star of mass 3.83×10^{30} kg.

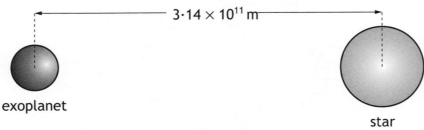

exoplanet

star

not to scale

(a) (i) Compare the mass of the star with the mass of the exoplanet in terms of orders of magnitude.

Space for working and answer

2

(ii) The distance between the exoplanet and the star is 3.14×10^{11} m.

Calculate the gravitational force between the star and the exoplanet.

Space for working and answer

3

MARKS | DO NOT WRITE IN THIS MARGIN

5. (continued)

(b) The gravitational force between the star and the exoplanet causes the star to follow a circular path as the exoplanet orbits the star. Small differences in the wavelength of the light from the star are observed on Earth.

Light from the star is redshifted when the star moves away from the Earth and blueshifted when the star moves towards the Earth.

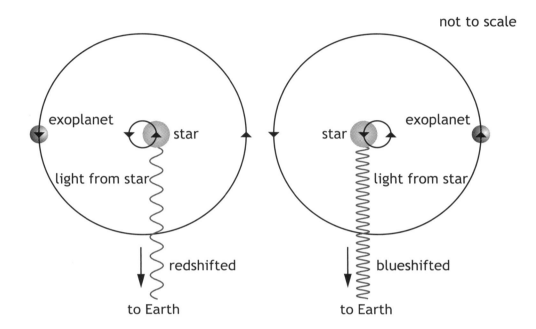

not to scale

(i) Calculate the redshift of light from the star observed on Earth when the star is moving away from the Earth at $6 \cdot 60 \times 10^3 \, \text{m s}^{-1}$.

Space for working and answer

3

(ii) For an exoplanet of greater mass at the same distance from the star, suggest whether the radius of the circular path followed by the star would be greater than, less than, or the same as that for an exoplanet of smaller mass.

1

MARKS | DO NOT WRITE IN THIS MARGIN

6. The visible spectrum of light emitted by a star is observed to contain a number of dark lines. The dark lines occur because certain wavelengths of light are absorbed when light passes through atoms in the star's outer atmosphere.

The diagram shows some of the energy levels for a hydrogen atom.

E_3 ——————————————— $-1{\cdot}36 \times 10^{-19}$ J

E_2 ——————————————— $-2{\cdot}42 \times 10^{-19}$ J

E_1 ——————————————— $-5{\cdot}42 \times 10^{-19}$ J

E_0 ——————————————— $-21{\cdot}8 \times 10^{-19}$ J

(a) For the energy levels shown in the diagram, identify the electron transition that would lead to the absorption of a photon with the highest frequency.   **1**

(b) An electron makes the transition from energy level E_1 to E_3.

Determine the frequency of the photon absorbed.   **3**

Space for working and answer

[Turn over for next question

DO NOT WRITE ON THIS PAGE

MARKS | DO NOT WRITE IN THIS MARGIN

7. The following diagram gives information on the Standard Model of fundamental particles.

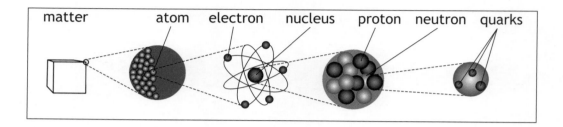

(a) Explain why the proton and the neutron are **not** fundamental particles.   1

(b) An extract from a data book contains the following information about three types of sigma (Σ) particles. Sigma particles are made up of three quarks.

Particle	Symbol	Quark Content	Charge	Mean lifetime (s)
sigma plus	Σ^+	up up strange	$+1e$	$8 \cdot 0 \times 10^{-11}$
neutral sigma	Σ^0	up down strange	0	$7 \cdot 4 \times 10^{-20}$
sigma minus	Σ^-	down down strange	$-1e$	$1 \cdot 5 \times 10^{-10}$

(i) A student makes the following statement.

All baryons are hadrons, but not all hadrons are baryons.

Explain why this statement is correct.   2

(ii) The charge on an up quark is $+\frac{2}{3}e$.

Determine the charge on a strange quark.   1

Space for working and answer

MARKS | DO NOT WRITE IN THIS MARGIN

7. (continued)

(c) (i) State the name of the force that holds the quarks together in the sigma (Σ) particle.   1

(ii) State the name of the boson associated with this force.   1

(d) Sigma minus (Σ^-) particles have a mean lifetime of $1 \cdot 5 \times 10^{-10}$ s in their frame of reference.

Σ^- are produced in a particle accelerator and travel at a speed of $0 \cdot 9c$ relative to a stationary observer.

Calculate the mean lifetime of the Σ^- particle as measured by this observer.   3

Space for working and answer

MARKS | DO NOT WRITE IN THIS MARGIN

8. X-ray machines are used in hospitals.

An X-ray machine contains a linear accelerator that is used to accelerate electrons towards a metal target.

The linear accelerator consists of hollow metal tubes placed in a vacuum.

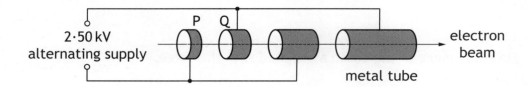

Electrons are accelerated across the gaps between the tubes by an alternating supply.

(a)   (i)   Calculate the work done on an electron as it accelerates from P to Q.   3

Space for working and answer

(ii)   Explain why an alternating supply is used in the linear accelerator.   1

MARKS | DO NOT WRITE IN THIS MARGIN

8. **(continued)**

(b) The electron beam is then passed into a "slalom magnet" beam guide. The function of the beam guide is to direct the electrons towards a metal target.

Inside the beam guides R and S, two different magnetic fields act on the electrons.

Electrons strike the metal target to produce high energy photons of radiation.

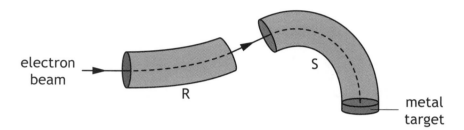

(i) Determine the direction of the magnetic field inside beam guide R. **1**

(ii) State **two** differences between the magnetic fields inside beam guides R and S. **2**

(c) Calculate the minimum speed of an electron that will produce a photon of energy $4 \cdot 16 \times 10^{-17}$ J. **3**

Space for working and answer

MARKS | DO NOT WRITE IN THIS MARGIN

9. A diagram from a 'How Things Work' website contains information about a nuclear fusion reaction.

Reaction of helium-3 with deuterium

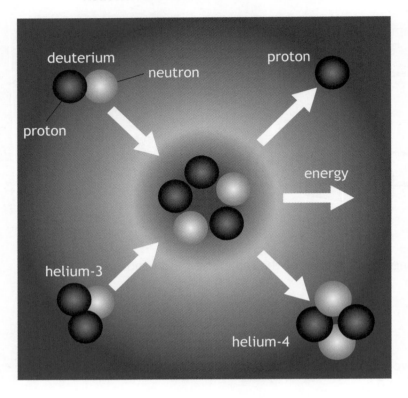

(a) State what is meant by the term *nuclear fusion*.   1

MARKS | DO NOT WRITE IN THIS MARGIN

9. (continued)

(b) The following statement represents this fusion reaction.

$$^{3}_{2}\text{He} + ^{2}_{1}\text{H} \rightarrow ^{4}_{2}\text{He} + ^{1}_{1}\text{p}$$

The mass of the particles involved in the reaction are shown in the table.

Particle	Mass (kg)
$^{3}_{2}\text{He}$	$5{\cdot}008 \times 10^{-27}$
$^{2}_{1}\text{H}$	$3{\cdot}344 \times 10^{-27}$
$^{4}_{2}\text{He}$	$6{\cdot}646 \times 10^{-27}$
$^{1}_{1}\text{p}$	$1{\cdot}673 \times 10^{-27}$

(i) Explain why energy is released in this reaction.   1

(ii) Determine the energy released in this reaction.   4

Space for working and answer

MARKS | DO NOT WRITE IN THIS MARGIN

10. An experiment is carried out to determine the wavelength of light from a laser.

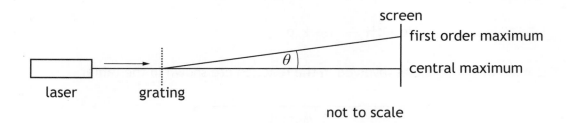

not to scale

(a) Explain, in terms of waves, how a maximum is formed.   1

(b) The experiment is carried out with four gratings.

The separation of the slits d is different for each grating.

The angle between the central maximum and the first order maximum θ, produced by each grating, is measured.

The results are used to produce a graph of $\sin\theta$ against $\dfrac{1}{d}$.

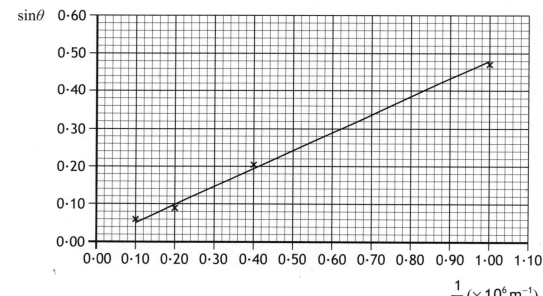

$\dfrac{1}{d} (\times 10^6 \, \text{m}^{-1})$

MARKS | DO NOT WRITE IN THIS MARGIN

10. **(b)** **(continued)**

(i) Determine the wavelength of the light from the laser used in this experiment.

Space for working and answer

3

(ii) Determine the angle θ produced when a grating with a spacing d of $2 \cdot 0 \times 10^{-6}$ m is used with this laser.

Space for working and answer

3

(c) Suggest **two** improvements that could be made to the experiment to improve reliability.

2

MARKS | DO NOT WRITE IN THIS MARGIN

11. The use of analogies from everyday life can help better understanding of physics concepts. A car moving from a smooth surface to a rough surface, eg from a road to sand, can be used as an analogy for the refraction of light.

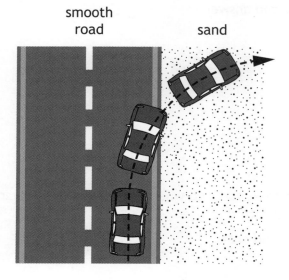

smooth
road   sand

Use your knowledge of physics to comment on this analogy.   3

[Turn over for next question

DO NOT WRITE ON THIS PAGE

MARKS | DO NOT WRITE IN THIS MARGIN

.ted to a battery containing two cells as shown.

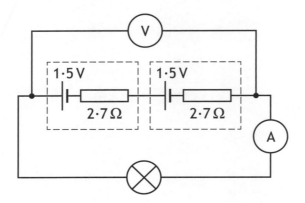

The e.m.f. of each cell is 1·5 V and the internal resistance of each cell is 2·7 Ω. The reading on the ammeter is 64 mA.

(a) State what is meant by *an e.m.f. of 1·5 V.*   **1**

(b)   (i) Show that the lost volts in the battery is 0·35 V.   **2**
           Space for working and answer

      (ii) Determine the reading on the voltmeter.   **1**
            Space for working and answer

      (iii) Calculate the power dissipated by the lamp.   **3**
             Space for working and answer

MARKS | DO NOT WRITE IN THIS MARGIN

12.   (continued)

(c) In a different circuit, an LED is connected to a battery containing four cells.

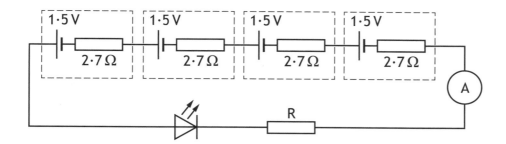

The potential difference across the LED is 3·6 V when the current is 26 mA.

Determine the resistance of resistor R.

Space for working and answer

4

[BLANK PAGE]

DO NOT WRITE ON THIS PAGE

MARKS | DO NOT WRITE IN THIS MARGIN

13. An uncharged 220 µF capacitor is connected in a circuit as shown.

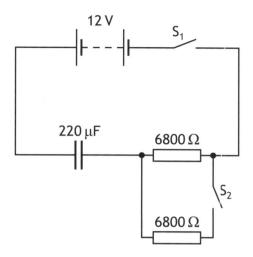

The 12 V battery has negligible internal resistance.

(a) Switch S_1 is closed and the capacitor charges in a time of 7·5 s.

Calculate the initial charging current.

Space for working and answer

3

(b) Switch S_1 is opened.

The capacitor is discharged.

Switch S_2 is now closed and then switch S_1 is closed.

Explain why the time for the capacitor to fully charge is less than in part (a).

2

MARKS

DO NOT WRITE IN THIS MARGIN

14. Solar cells are made by joining n-type and p-type semiconductor materials. A layer is formed at the junction between the materials.

    (a) A potential difference is produced when photons enter the layer between the p-type and n-type materials.

    State the name of this effect.

    1

    (b) A student carries out an experiment using a solar cell connected to a variable resistor R as shown.

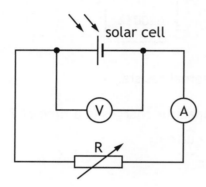

    A lamp is placed above the solar cell and switched on.

    The variable resistor is altered and readings of current and voltage are taken. These readings are used to produce the following graph.

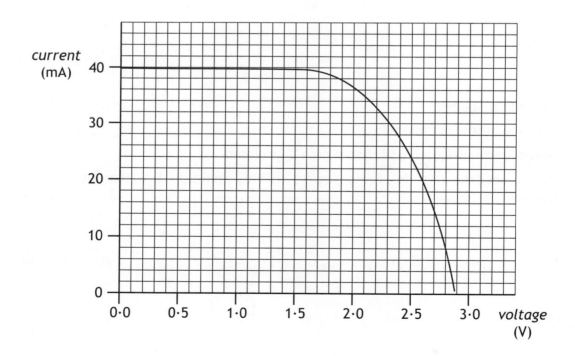

MARKS | DO NOT WRITE IN THIS MARGIN

14. (b) (continued)

    (i) Solar cells have a maximum power output for a particular irradiance of light.

       In this experiment, the maximum power output occurs when the voltage is 2·1 V.

       Use information from the graph to estimate a value for the maximum power output from the solar cell.

       Space for working and answer

       3

    (ii) The lamp is now moved closer to the solar cell.

       Explain, in terms of photons, why the maximum output power from the solar cell increases.

       1

MARKS | DO NOT WRITE IN THIS MARGIN

15. A wire of length L and cross-sectional area A is shown.

A — wire

L

The resistance R of the wire is given by the relationship

$$R = \frac{\rho L}{A}$$

where ρ is the resistivity of the wire in $\Omega\,$m.

(a) The resistivity of aluminium is $2\cdot 8 \times 10^{-8}\,\Omega\,$m.

Calculate the resistance of an aluminium wire of length $0\cdot 82\,$m and cross-sectional area $4\cdot 0 \times 10^{-6}\,$m^2.

Space for working and answer

2

MARKS | DO NOT WRITE IN THIS MARGIN

15. (continued)

(b) A student carries out an investigation to determine the resistivity of a cylindrical metal wire of cross-sectional area $4 \cdot 52 \times 10^{-6} \, m^2$.

$4 \cdot 52 \times 10^{-6} \, m^2$ —

The student varies the length L of the wire and measures the corresponding resistance R of the wire.

The results are shown in the table.

Length of wire L (m)	Resistance of wire R ($\times 10^{-3} \, \Omega$)
1·5	5·6
2·0	7·5
2·5	9·4
3·0	11·2
3·5	13·2

(i) Using the square-ruled paper on *Page thirty-six*, draw a graph of R against L. **3**

(ii) Calculate the gradient of your graph. **2**

Space for working and answer

(iii) Determine the resistivity of the metal wire. **3**

Space for working and answer

[END OF QUESTION PAPER]

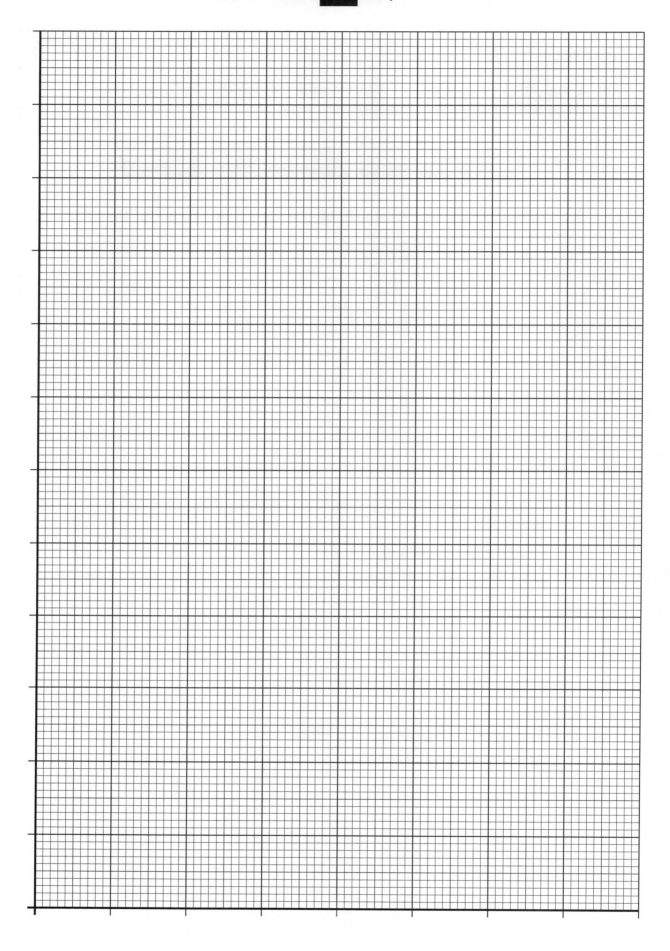

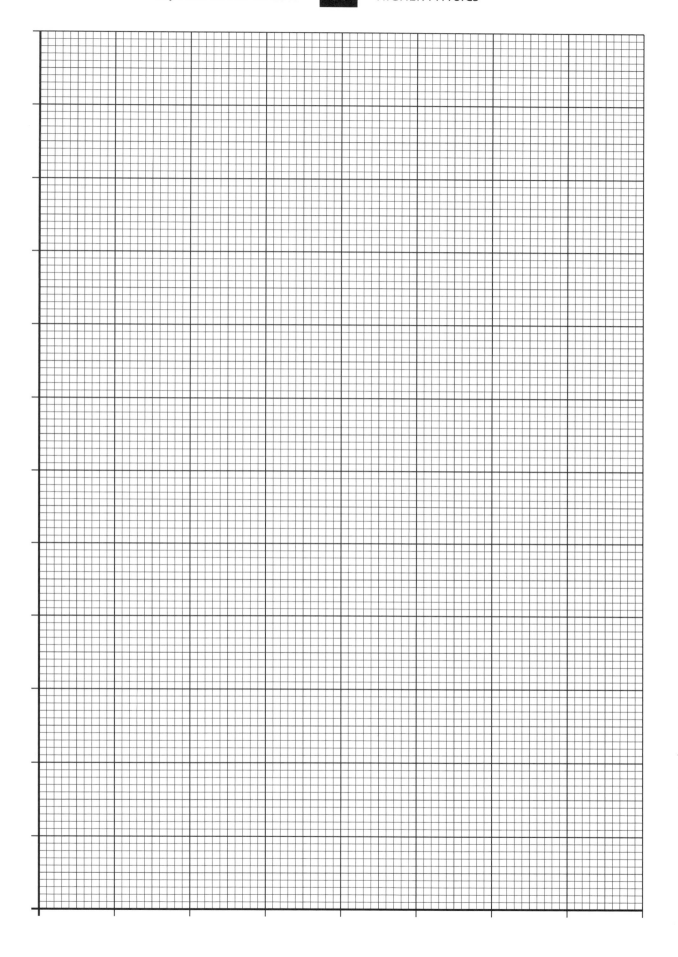

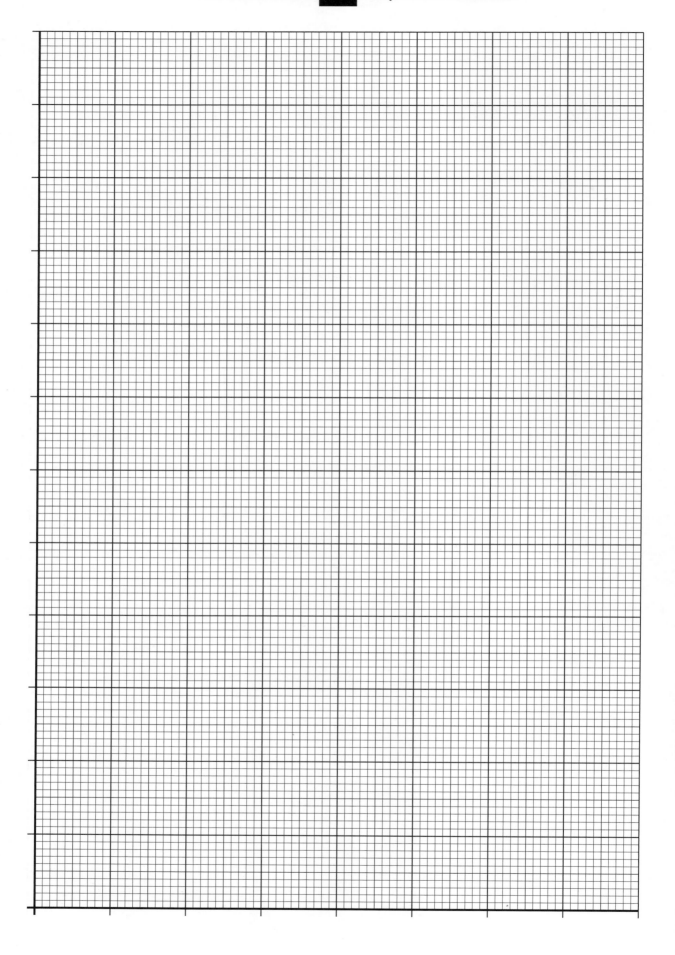

MARKS | DO NOT WRITE IN THIS MARGIN

ADDITIONAL SPACE FOR ANSWERS AND ROUGH WORK

Additional graph for use with Question 3 (b)

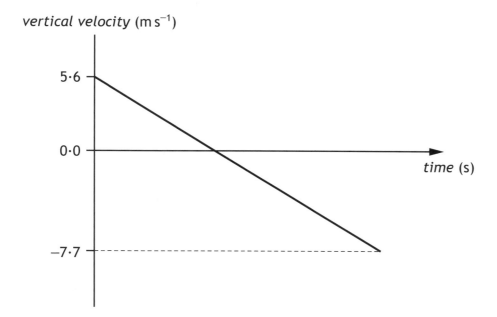

ADDITIONAL SPACE FOR ANSWERS AND ROUGH WORK

HIGHER

2018

National
Qualifications
2018

X757/76/02

**Physics
Section 1 — Questions**

TUESDAY, 8 MAY

9:00 AM – 11:30 AM

Instructions for the completion of Section 1 are given on *Page two* of your question and answer booklet X757/76/01.

Record your answers on the answer grid on *Page three* of your question and answer booklet.

Reference may be made to the Data Sheet on *Page two* of this booklet and to the Relationships Sheet X757/76/11.

Before leaving the examination room you must give your question and answer booklet to the Invigilator; if you do not, you may lose all the marks for this paper.

DATA SHEET

COMMON PHYSICAL QUANTITIES

Quantity	Symbol	Value	Quantity	Symbol	Value
Speed of light in vacuum	c	$3.00 \times 10^8\,\mathrm{m\,s^{-1}}$	Planck's constant	h	$6.63 \times 10^{-34}\,\mathrm{J\,s}$
Magnitude of the charge on an electron	e	$1.60 \times 10^{-19}\,\mathrm{C}$	Mass of electron	m_e	$9.11 \times 10^{-31}\,\mathrm{kg}$
Universal Constant of Gravitation	G	$6.67 \times 10^{-11}\,\mathrm{m^3\,kg^{-1}\,s^{-2}}$	Mass of neutron	m_n	$1.675 \times 10^{-27}\,\mathrm{kg}$
Gravitational acceleration on Earth	g	$9.8\,\mathrm{m\,s^{-2}}$	Mass of proton	m_p	$1.673 \times 10^{-27}\,\mathrm{kg}$
Hubble's constant	H_0	$2.3 \times 10^{-18}\,\mathrm{s^{-1}}$			

REFRACTIVE INDICES

The refractive indices refer to sodium light of wavelength 589 nm and to substances at a temperature of 273 K.

Substance	Refractive index	Substance	Refractive index
Diamond	2·42	Water	1·33
Crown glass	1·50	Air	1·00

SPECTRAL LINES

Element	Wavelength/nm	Colour	Element	Wavelength/nm	Colour
Hydrogen	656	Red	Cadmium	644	Red
	486	Blue-green		509	Green
	434	Blue-violet		480	Blue
	410	Violet		Lasers	
	397	Ultraviolet	Element	Wavelength/nm	Colour
	389	Ultraviolet	Carbon dioxide	9550 / 10590	Infrared
Sodium	589	Yellow	Helium-neon	633	Red

PROPERTIES OF SELECTED MATERIALS

Substance	Density/kg m⁻³	Melting Point/K	Boiling Point/K
Aluminium	2.70×10^3	933	2623
Copper	8.96×10^3	1357	2853
Ice	9.20×10^2	273	. . . .
Sea Water	1.02×10^3	264	377
Water	1.00×10^3	273	373
Air	1·29	. . . .	. . . .
Hydrogen	9.0×10^{-2}	14	20

The gas densities refer to a temperature of 273 K and a pressure of 1.01×10^5 Pa.

SECTION 1 — 20 marks
Attempt ALL questions

1. A car is moving at a speed of $2 \cdot 0 \, \text{m s}^{-1}$.

    The car now accelerates at $4 \cdot 0 \, \text{m s}^{-2}$ until it reaches a speed of $14 \, \text{m s}^{-1}$.

    The distance travelled by the car during this acceleration is

    A $1 \cdot 5 \, \text{m}$

    B $18 \, \text{m}$

    C $24 \, \text{m}$

    D $25 \, \text{m}$

    E $48 \, \text{m}$.

2. A ball is dropped from rest and allowed to bounce several times.

    The graph shows how the velocity of the ball varies with time.

    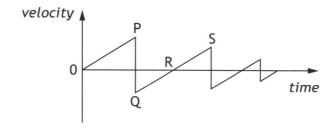

    A student makes the following statements about the ball.

    I   The ball hits the ground at P.

    II   The ball is moving upwards between Q and R.

    III   The ball is moving upwards between R and S.

    Which of these statements is/are correct?

    A   I only

    B   II only

    C   III only

    D   I and II only

    E   I and III only

[Turn over

3. A block of mass 6·0 kg and a block of mass 8·0 kg are connected by a string.

   A force of 32 N is applied to the blocks as shown.

   A frictional force of 4·0 N acts on **each** block.

   The acceleration of the 6·0 kg block is

   A $1·7\,m\,s^{-2}$

   B $2·0\,m\,s^{-2}$

   C $2·3\,m\,s^{-2}$

   D $2·9\,m\,s^{-2}$

   E $5·3\,m\,s^{-2}$.

4. A person stands on a weighing machine in a lift. When the lift is at rest, the reading on the weighing machine is 700 N.

   The lift now descends and its speed increases at a constant rate.

   The reading on the weighing machine

   A is a constant value higher than 700 N

   B is a constant value lower than 700 N

   C continually increases from 700 N

   D continually decreases from 700 N

   E remains constant at 700 N.

5. Enceladus is a moon of Saturn. The mass of Enceladus is $1·08 \times 10^{20}$ kg.

   The mass of Saturn is $5·68 \times 10^{26}$ kg.

   The gravitational force of attraction between Enceladus and Saturn is $7·24 \times 10^{19}$ N.

   The orbital radius of Enceladus around Saturn is

   A $2·38 \times 10^{8}$ m

   B $9·11 \times 10^{13}$ m

   C $5·65 \times 10^{16}$ m

   D $8·30 \times 10^{27}$ m

   E $3·19 \times 10^{33}$ m.

6. A spacecraft is travelling at $0 \cdot 10c$ relative to a star.

   An observer on the spacecraft measures the speed of light emitted by the star to be

   A $0 \cdot 90c$

   B $0 \cdot 99c$

   C $1 \cdot 00c$

   D $1 \cdot 01c$

   E $1 \cdot 10c$.

7. A spacecraft is travelling at a speed of $0 \cdot 200c$ relative to the Earth.

   The spacecraft emits a signal for 20·0 seconds as measured in the frame of reference of the spacecraft.

   An observer on Earth measures the duration of the signal as

   A 19·2 s

   B 19·6 s

   C 20·0 s

   D 20·4 s

   E 20·8 s.

8. How many types of quark are there?

   A 8

   B 6

   C 4

   D 3

   E 2

9. An electron is a

   A boson

   B hadron

   C baryon

   D meson

   E lepton.

[Turn over

10. A proton enters a region of magnetic field as shown.

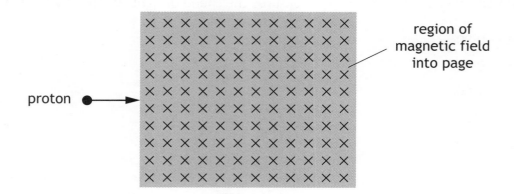

On entering the magnetic field the proton

A   deflects into the page

B   deflects out of the page

C   deflects towards the top of the page

D   deflects towards the bottom of the page

E   is not deflected.

11. A nuclear fission reaction is represented by the following statement.

$${}_{0}^{1}n + {}_{92}^{235}U \rightarrow {}_{56}^{141}Ba + X + 3\,{}_{0}^{1}n$$

The nucleus represented by X is

A ${}_{40}^{96}Zr$

B ${}_{36}^{92}Kr$

C ${}_{40}^{97}Zr$

D ${}_{36}^{93}Kr$

E ${}_{40}^{94}Zr$.

12. The irradiance on a surface 0·50 m from a point source of light is I.

The irradiance on a surface 1·5 m from this source is

A   0·11I

B   0·33I

C   1·5I

D   3·0I

E   9·0I.

13. Waves from two coherent sources, S_1 and S_2, produce an interference pattern. Maxima are detected at the positions shown below.

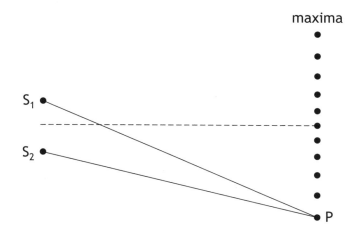

The path difference $S_1P - S_2P$ is 154 mm.

The wavelength of the waves is

A   15·4 mm

B   25·7 mm

C   28·0 mm

D   30·8 mm

E   34·2 mm.

[Turn over

14. A ray of monochromatic light passes from air into a block of glass as shown.

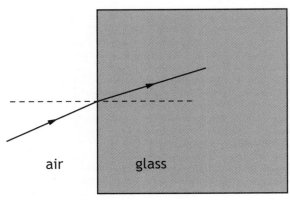

not to scale

air   glass

The wavelength of this light in air is $6\cdot30 \times 10^{-7}$ m.

The refractive index of the glass for this light is 1·50.

The frequency of this light in the glass is

A $2\cdot10 \times 10^{-15}$ Hz

B $1\cdot26 \times 10^{2}$ Hz

C $1\cdot89 \times 10^{2}$ Hz

D $4\cdot76 \times 10^{14}$ Hz

E $7\cdot14 \times 10^{14}$ Hz.

15. A circuit is set up as shown.

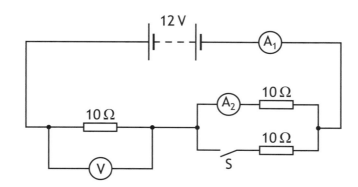

The battery has negligible internal resistance.

A student makes the following statements about the readings on the meters in this circuit.

I　When switch S is open the reading on the voltmeter will be 6·0 V.

II　When switch S is open the reading on A_2 will be 0·60 A.

III　When switch S is closed the reading on A_1 will be 0·80 A.

Which of these statements is/are correct?

A　I only

B　II only

C　I and II only

D　II and III only

E　I, II and III

16. The power dissipated in a 120 Ω resistor is 4·8 W.

The current in the resistor is

A　0·020 A

B　0·040 A

C　0·20 A

D　5·0 A

E　25 A.

[Turn over

17. A 24·0 μF capacitor is charged until the potential difference across it is 125 V.
     The charge stored on the capacitor is

     A $5·21 \times 10^{6}$ C

     B $7·75 \times 10^{-2}$ C

     C $1·50 \times 10^{-3}$ C

     D $3·00 \times 10^{-3}$ C

     E $1·92 \times 10^{-7}$ C.

18. A circuit is set up as shown.

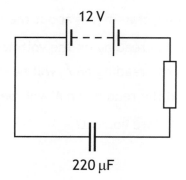

     When the capacitor is fully charged the energy stored in the capacitor is

     A $1·6 \times 10^{-5}$ J

     B $1·3 \times 10^{-3}$ J

     C $2·6 \times 10^{-3}$ J

     D $1·6 \times 10^{-2}$ J

     E $1·6 \times 10^{4}$ J.

19. The circuit shown is used to charge and then discharge a capacitor C.

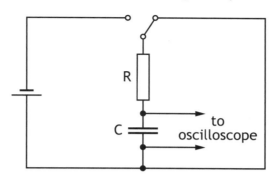

Which pair of graphs shows how the potential difference V across the capacitor varies with time t during charging and discharging?

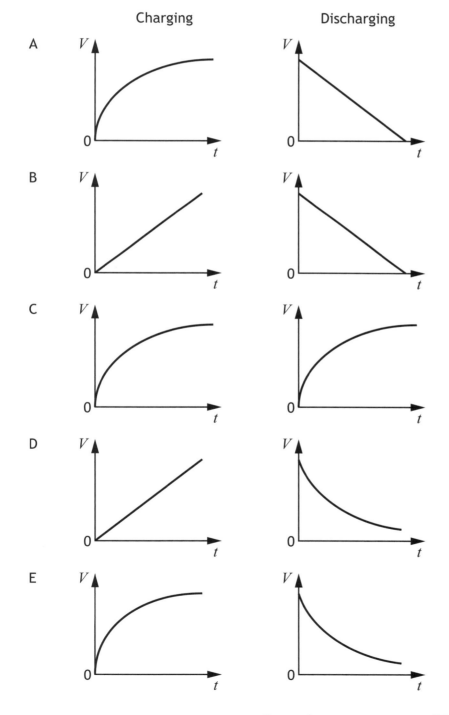

20. A student carries out an experiment to determine the specific heat capacity c of a solid.

The relationship used to calculate c is

$$c = \frac{E}{m\Delta T}$$

The recorded measurements and their percentage uncertainties are shown.

energy supplied, $E = 5000\,\text{J} \pm 1\%$

mass of solid, $m = 0\cdot20\,\text{kg} \pm 2\%$

change in temperature, $\Delta T = 4\cdot5\,^{\circ}\text{C} \pm 5\%$

A good estimate of the percentage uncertainty in the calculated value of c is

A   8%

B   7%

C   5%

D   3%

E   1%.

[END OF SECTION 1. NOW ATTEMPT THE QUESTIONS IN SECTION 2 OF YOUR QUESTION AND ANSWER BOOKLET]

National Qualifications 2018

X757/76/11

Physics
Relationship Sheet

TUESDAY, 8 MAY
9:00 AM – 11:30 AM

Relationships required for Physics Higher

$d = \bar{v}t$

$s = \bar{v}t$

$v = u + at$

$s = ut + \frac{1}{2}at^2$

$v^2 = u^2 + 2as$

$s = \frac{1}{2}(u+v)t$

$W = mg$

$F = ma$

$E_W = Fd$

$E_p = mgh$

$E_k = \frac{1}{2}mv^2$

$P = \dfrac{E}{t}$

$p = mv$

$Ft = mv - mu$

$F = G\dfrac{m_1 m_2}{r^2}$

$t' = \dfrac{t}{\sqrt{1-\left(\frac{v}{c}\right)^2}}$

$l' = l\sqrt{1-\left(\frac{v}{c}\right)^2}$

$f_o = f_s\left(\dfrac{v}{v \pm v_s}\right)$

$z = \dfrac{\lambda_{observed} - \lambda_{rest}}{\lambda_{rest}}$

$z = \dfrac{v}{c}$

$v = H_0 d$

$W = QV$

$E = mc^2$

$E = hf$

$E_k = hf - hf_0$

$E_2 - E_1 = hf$

$T = \dfrac{1}{f}$

$v = f\lambda$

$d\sin\theta = m\lambda$

$n = \dfrac{\sin\theta_1}{\sin\theta_2}$

$\dfrac{\sin\theta_1}{\sin\theta_2} = \dfrac{\lambda_1}{\lambda_2} = \dfrac{v_1}{v_2}$

$\sin\theta_c = \dfrac{1}{n}$

$I = \dfrac{k}{d^2}$

$I = \dfrac{P}{A}$

path difference $= m\lambda$ or $\left(m+\frac{1}{2}\right)\lambda$ where $m = 0,1,2...$

random uncertainty $= \dfrac{\text{max. value} - \text{min. value}}{\text{number of values}}$

$V_{peak} = \sqrt{2}V_{rms}$

$I_{peak} = \sqrt{2}I_{rms}$

$Q = It$

$V = IR$

$P = IV = I^2 R = \dfrac{V^2}{R}$

$R_T = R_1 + R_2 + ...$

$\dfrac{1}{R_T} = \dfrac{1}{R_1} + \dfrac{1}{R_2} + ...$

$E = V + Ir$

$V_1 = \left(\dfrac{R_1}{R_1 + R_2}\right)V_s$

$\dfrac{V_1}{V_2} = \dfrac{R_1}{R_2}$

$C = \dfrac{Q}{V}$

$E = \frac{1}{2}QV = \frac{1}{2}CV^2 = \frac{1}{2}\dfrac{Q^2}{C}$

Additional Relationships

Circle

$\text{circumference} = 2\pi r$

$\text{area} = \pi r^2$

Sphere

$\text{area} = 4\pi r^2$

$\text{volume} = \frac{4}{3}\pi r^3$

Trigonometry

$\sin\theta = \dfrac{\text{opposite}}{\text{hypotenuse}}$

$\cos\theta = \dfrac{\text{adjacent}}{\text{hypotenuse}}$

$\tan\theta = \dfrac{\text{opposite}}{\text{adjacent}}$

$\sin^2\theta + \cos^2\theta = 1$

Electron Arrangements of Elements

Key

| Atomic number |
| Symbol |
| Electron arrangement |
| Name |

Group 1

Atomic number	Symbol	Electron arrangement	Name
1	H	1	Hydrogen
3	Li	2,1	Lithium
11	Na	2,8,1	Sodium
19	K	2,8,8,1	Potassium
37	Rb	2,8,18,8,1	Rubidium
55	Cs	2,8,18,18,8,1	Caesium
87	Fr	2,8,18,32,18,8,1	Francium

Group 2

Atomic number	Symbol	Electron arrangement	Name
4	Be	2,2	Beryllium
12	Mg	2,8,2	Magnesium
20	Ca	2,8,8,2	Calcium
38	Sr	2,8,18,8,2	Strontium
56	Ba	2,8,18,18,8,2	Barium
88	Ra	2,8,18,32,18,8,2	Radium

Transition Elements

Group	Atomic number	Symbol	Electron arrangement	Name
(3)	21	Sc	2,8,9,2	Scandium
(3)	39	Y	2,8,18,9,2	Yttrium
(3)	57	La	2,8,18,18,9,2	Lanthanum
(3)	89	Ac	2,8,18,32,18,9,2	Actinium
(4)	22	Ti	2,8,10,2	Titanium
(4)	40	Zr	2,8,18,10,2	Zirconium
(4)	72	Hf	2,8,18,32,10,2	Hafnium
(4)	104	Rf	2,8,18,32,32,10,2	Rutherfordium
(5)	23	V	2,8,11,2	Vanadium
(5)	41	Nb	2,8,18,12,1	Niobium
(5)	73	Ta	2,8,18,32,11,2	Tantalum
(5)	105	Db	2,8,18,32,32,11,2	Dubnium
(6)	24	Cr	2,8,13,1	Chromium
(6)	42	Mo	2,8,18,13,1	Molybdenum
(6)	74	W	2,8,18,32,12,2	Tungsten
(6)	106	Sg	2,8,18,32,32,12,2	Seaborgium
(7)	25	Mn	2,8,13,2	Manganese
(7)	43	Tc	2,8,18,13,2	Technetium
(7)	75	Re	2,8,18,32,13,2	Rhenium
(7)	107	Bh	2,8,18,32,32,13,2	Bohrium
(8)	26	Fe	2,8,14,2	Iron
(8)	44	Ru	2,8,18,15,1	Ruthenium
(8)	76	Os	2,8,18,32,14,2	Osmium
(8)	108	Hs	2,8,18,32,32,14,2	Hassium
(9)	27	Co	2,8,15,2	Cobalt
(9)	45	Rh	2,8,18,16,1	Rhodium
(9)	77	Ir	2,8,18,32,15,2	Iridium
(9)	109	Mt	2,8,18,32,32,15,2	Meitnerium
(10)	28	Ni	2,8,16,2	Nickel
(10)	46	Pd	2,8,18,18,0	Palladium
(10)	78	Pt	2,8,18,32,17,1	Platinum
(10)	110	Ds	2,8,18,32,32,17,1	Darmstadtium
(11)	29	Cu	2,8,18,1	Copper
(11)	47	Ag	2,8,18,18,1	Silver
(11)	79	Au	2,8,18,32,18,1	Gold
(11)	111	Rg	2,8,18,32,32,18,1	Roentgenium
(12)	30	Zn	2,8,18,2	Zinc
(12)	48	Cd	2,8,18,18,2	Cadmium
(12)	80	Hg	2,8,18,32,18,2	Mercury
(12)	112	Cn	2,8,18,32,32,18,2	Copernicium

Group 3 (13)

Atomic number	Symbol	Electron arrangement	Name
5	B	2,3	Boron
13	Al	2,8,3	Aluminium
31	Ga	2,8,18,3	Gallium
49	In	2,8,18,18,3	Indium
81	Tl	2,8,18,32,18,3	Thallium

Group 4 (14)

Atomic number	Symbol	Electron arrangement	Name
6	C	2,4	Carbon
14	Si	2,8,4	Silicon
32	Ge	2,8,18,4	Germanium
50	Sn	2,8,18,18,4	Tin
82	Pb	2,8,18,32,18,4	Lead

Group 5 (15)

Atomic number	Symbol	Electron arrangement	Name
7	N	2,5	Nitrogen
15	P	2,8,5	Phosphorus
33	As	2,8,18,5	Arsenic
51	Sb	2,8,18,18,5	Antimony
83	Bi	2,8,18,32,18,5	Bismuth

Group 6 (16)

Atomic number	Symbol	Electron arrangement	Name
8	O	2,6	Oxygen
16	S	2,8,6	Sulfur
34	Se	2,8,18,6	Selenium
52	Te	2,8,18,18,6	Tellurium
84	Po	2,8,18,32,18,6	Polonium

Group 7 (17)

Atomic number	Symbol	Electron arrangement	Name
9	F	2,7	Fluorine
17	Cl	2,8,7	Chlorine
35	Br	2,8,18,7	Bromine
53	I	2,8,18,18,7	Iodine
85	At	2,8,18,32,18,7	Astatine

Group 0 (18)

Atomic number	Symbol	Electron arrangement	Name
2	He	2	Helium
10	Ne	2,8	Neon
18	Ar	2,8,8	Argon
36	Kr	2,8,18,8	Krypton
54	Xe	2,8,18,18,8	Xenon
86	Rn	2,8,18,32,18,8	Radon

Lanthanides

Atomic number	Symbol	Electron arrangement	Name
57	La	2,8,18,18,9,2	Lanthanum
58	Ce	2,8,18,20,8,2	Cerium
59	Pr	2,8,18,21,8,2	Praseodymium
60	Nd	2,8,18,22,8,2	Neodymium
61	Pm	2,8,18,23,8,2	Promethium
62	Sm	2,8,18,24,8,2	Samarium
63	Eu	2,8,18,25,8,2	Europium
64	Gd	2,8,18,25,9,2	Gadolinium
65	Tb	2,8,18,27,8,2	Terbium
66	Dy	2,8,18,28,8,2	Dysprosium
67	Ho	2,8,18,29,8,2	Holmium
68	Er	2,8,18,30,8,2	Erbium
69	Tm	2,8,18,31,8,2	Thulium
70	Yb	2,8,18,32,8,2	Ytterbium
71	Lu	2,8,18,32,9,2	Lutetium

Actinides

Atomic number	Symbol	Electron arrangement	Name
89	Ac	2,8,18,32,18,9,2	Actinium
90	Th	2,8,18,32,18,10,2	Thorium
91	Pa	2,8,18,32,20,9,2	Protactinium
92	U	2,8,18,32,21,9,2	Uranium
93	Np	2,8,18,32,22,9,2	Neptunium
94	Pu	2,8,18,32,24,8,2	Plutonium
95	Am	2,8,18,32,25,8,2	Americium
96	Cm	2,8,18,32,25,9,2	Curium
97	Bk	2,8,18,32,27,8,2	Berkelium
98	Cf	2,8,18,32,28,8,2	Californium
99	Es	2,8,18,32,29,8,2	Einsteinium
100	Fm	2,8,18,32,30,8,2	Fermium
101	Md	2,8,18,32,31,8,2	Mendelevium
102	No	2,8,18,32,32,8,2	Nobelium
103	Lr	2,8,18,32,32,9,2	Lawrencium

FOR OFFICIAL USE

National
Qualifications
2018

Mark

X757/76/01

**Physics
Section 1 — Answer Grid
and Section 2**

TUESDAY, 8 MAY

9:00 AM – 11:30 AM

Fill in these boxes and read what is printed below.

Full name of centre

Town

Forename(s)

Surname

Number of seat

Date of birth

Day   Month   Year

Scottish candidate number

Total marks — 130

SECTION 1 — 20 marks
Attempt ALL questions.
Instructions for the completion of Section 1 are given on *Page two*.

SECTION 2 — 110 marks
Attempt ALL questions.

Reference may be made to the Data Sheet on *Page two* of the question paper X757/76/02 and to the Relationships Sheet X757/76/11.

Care should be taken to give an appropriate number of significant figures in the final answers to calculations.

Write your answers clearly in the spaces provided in this booklet. Additional space for answers and rough work is provided at the end of this booklet. If you use this space you must clearly identify the question number you are attempting. Any rough work must be written in this booklet. You should score through your rough work when you have written your final copy.

Use **blue** or **black** ink.

Before leaving the examination room you must give this booklet to the Invigilator; if you do not, you may lose all the marks for this paper.

The questions for Section 1 are contained in the question paper X757/76/02.

Read these and record your answers on the answer grid on *Page three* opposite.

Use **blue** or **black** ink. Do NOT use gel pens or pencil.

1. The answer to each question is **either** A, B, C, D or E. Decide what your answer is, then fill in the appropriate bubble (see sample question below).

2. There is **only one correct** answer to each question.

3. Any rough working should be done on the additional space for answers and rough work at the end of this booklet.

Sample question

The energy unit measured by the electricity meter in your home is the

    A   ampere

    B   kilowatt-hour

    C   watt

    D   coulomb

    E   volt.

The correct answer is **B** — kilowatt-hour. The answer **B** bubble has been clearly filled in (see below).

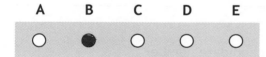

Changing an answer

If you decide to change your answer, cancel your first answer by putting a cross through it (see below) and fill in the answer you want. The answer below has been changed to **D**.

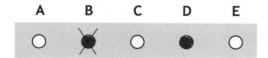

If you then decide to change back to an answer you have already scored out, put a tick (✓) to the **right** of the answer you want, as shown below:

SECTION 1 — Answer Grid

	A	B	C	D	E
1	○	○	○	○	○
2	○	○	○	○	○
3	○	○	○	○	○
4	○	○	○	○	○
5	○	○	○	○	○
6	○	○	○	○	○
7	○	○	○	○	○
8	○	○	○	○	○
9	○	○	○	○	○
10	○	○	○	○	○
11	○	○	○	○	○
12	○	○	○	○	○
13	○	○	○	○	○
14	○	○	○	○	○
15	○	○	○	○	○
16	○	○	○	○	○
17	○	○	○	○	○
18	○	○	○	○	○
19	○	○	○	○	○
20	○	○	○	○	○

[BLANK PAGE]

DO NOT WRITE ON THIS PAGE

[Turn over for SECTION 2

DO NOT WRITE ON THIS PAGE

MARKS | DO NOT WRITE IN THIS MARGIN

SECTION 2 — 110 marks

Attempt ALL questions

1. During a school funfair, a student throws a wet sponge at a teacher. The sponge is thrown with an initial velocity of $7 \cdot 4\,\text{m s}^{-1}$ at an angle of 30° to the horizontal.

    The sponge leaves the student's hand at a height of $1 \cdot 5\,\text{m}$ above the ground.

    not to scale

    The sponge hits the teacher.

    The effects of air resistance can be ignored.

    (a) (i) Calculate:

         (A) the horizontal component of the initial velocity of the sponge;   **1**

              Space for working and answer

         (B) the vertical component of the initial velocity of the sponge.   **1**

              Space for working and answer

MARKS | DO NOT WRITE IN THIS MARGIN

1. (a) (continued)

(ii) Calculate the time taken for the sponge to reach its maximum height.

Space for working and answer

3

(iii) The sponge takes a further 0·45 s to travel from its maximum height until it hits the teacher.

Determine the height h above the ground at which the sponge hits the teacher.

Space for working and answer

4

(b) The student throwing the sponge makes the following statement.

"If the sponge is thrown with a higher speed at the same angle from the same height then it would take a shorter time to hit the teacher in the same place."

Explain why the student's statement is incorrect.

2

MARKS | DO NOT WRITE IN THIS MARGIN

2. An internet shopping company is planning to use drones to deliver packages.

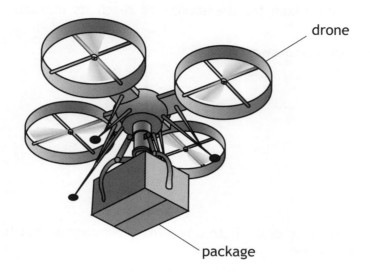

drone

package

(a) During a test the drone is hovering at a constant height above the ground.

The mass of the drone is 5·50 kg.

The mass of the package is 1·25 kg.

   (i) Determine the upward force produced by the drone.

     Space for working and answer

3

MARKS DO NOT WRITE IN THIS MARGIN

2. (a) (continued)

(ii) The package is now lowered using a motor and a cable.

A battery supplies 12 V across the motor. The resistance of the motor is 9·6 Ω.

Calculate the power dissipated by the motor.

Space for working and answer

3

(iii) While the package is being lowered the cable breaks.

The upward force produced by the drone remains constant.

Describe the vertical motion of the drone immediately after the cable breaks.

Justify your answer.

2

[Turn over

MARKS | DO NOT WRITE IN THIS MARGIN

2.   **(continued)**

(b) To carry a package with a greater mass two drones are used as shown.

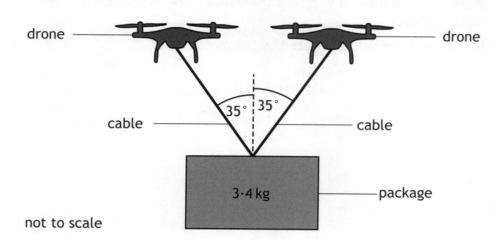

not to scale

The drones are hovering at a constant height above the ground.

The mass of the package suspended from the two drones is 3·4 kg.

Determine the tension in each cable.

Space for working and answer

4

[Turn over for next question

DO NOT WRITE ON THIS PAGE

3. A student sets up an experiment to investigate a collision between two vehicles on a frictionless air track.

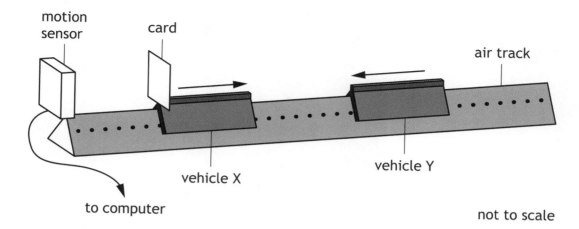

motion sensor

card

air track

to computer

vehicle X

vehicle Y

not to scale

Vehicle X of mass 0·75 kg is travelling to the right along the track.

Vehicle Y of mass 0·50 kg is travelling to the left along the track with a speed of 0·30 m s^{-1}.

The vehicles collide and move off separately.

A computer displays a graph showing the velocity of vehicle X from just before the collision to just after the collision.

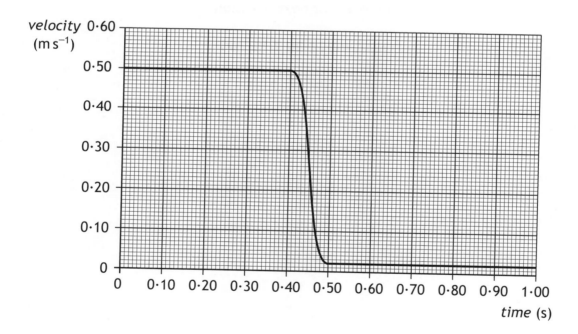

velocity (m s^{-1})

time (s)

MARKS | DO NOT WRITE IN THIS MARGIN

3. (continued)

(a) Show that the velocity of vehicle Y after the collision is $0.42\,\text{m s}^{-1}$.

Space for working and answer

2

(b) Determine the impulse on vehicle Y during the collision.

Space for working and answer

3

[Turn over

MARKS | DO NOT WRITE IN THIS MARGIN

3. (continued)

    (c) Explain how the student would determine whether the collision was elastic or inelastic.

2

MARKS | DO NOT WRITE IN THIS MARGIN

4. A stunt is being carried out during the making of a film.

A car is to be driven up a ramp on a moving lorry by a stunt driver, who will attempt to land the car safely on the roof of a second moving lorry. The car is to stop on the roof of the second lorry while this lorry is still moving.

Using your knowledge of physics, comment on the challenges involved in carrying out the stunt successfully.

3

[Turn over

MARKS | DO NOT WRITE IN THIS MARGIN

5. Hubble's Law states that the universe is expanding. The expanding universe is one piece of evidence that supports the Big Bang theory.

    (a) State one other piece of evidence that supports the Big Bang theory.   **1**

    (b) A student plots some of the original data from the 1929 paper by Edwin Hubble and adds the line shown in order to determine a value for the Hubble constant H_0.

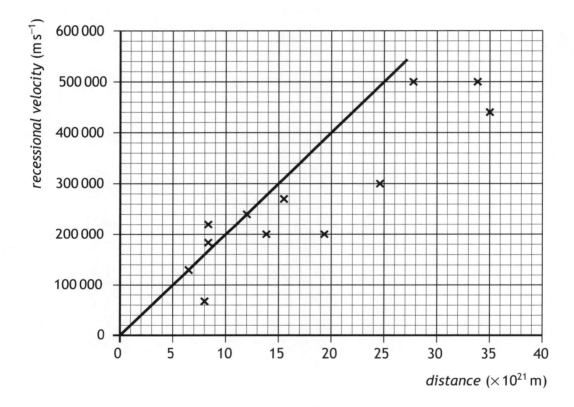

The student calculates the gradient of their line and obtains a value for the Hubble constant of $2 \cdot 0 \times 10^{-17}\,\text{s}^{-1}$.

The age of the universe can be calculated using the relationship

$$\text{age of universe} = \frac{1}{H_0}$$

MARKS | DO NOT WRITE IN THIS MARGIN

5. (b) (continued)

(i) Calculate the age of the universe, in years, obtained when using the student's value for the Hubble constant.

Space for working and answer

2

(ii) The current estimate for the age of the universe is $13\cdot8 \times 10^9$ years.

(A) State why the value obtained in (b)(i) is different from the current estimate for the age of the universe.

1

(B) Suggest a change that the student could make to their graph to obtain a value closer to the current estimate for the age of the universe.

1

(c) It has been discovered that the rate of expansion of the universe is increasing.

State what physicists think is responsible for this increase.

1

MARKS | DO NOT WRITE IN THIS MARGIN

6. An experiment is set up to demonstrate a simple particle accelerator.

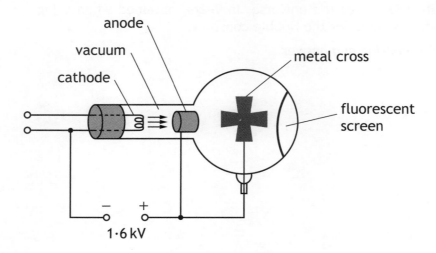

(a) Electrons are accelerated from rest between the cathode and the anode by a potential difference of 1·6 kV.

   (i) Show that the work done in accelerating an electron from rest is $2·6 \times 10^{-16}$ J.

   Space for working and answer

   2

   (ii) Calculate the speed of the electron as it reaches the anode.

   Space for working and answer

   3

MARKS | DO NOT WRITE IN THIS MARGIN

6. (continued)

(b) As the electrons travel through the vacuum towards the fluorescent screen they spread out.

In the path of the electrons there is a metal cross, which is connected to the positive terminal of the supply. The electrons that hit the cross are stopped by the metal.

Electrons that get past the metal cross hit a fluorescent screen at the far side of the tube.

When electrons hit the fluorescent screen, the screen glows.

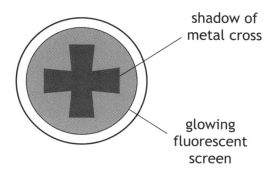

shadow of metal cross

glowing fluorescent screen

The potential difference between the anode and the cathode is now increased to 2·2 kV. This changes what is observed on the screen.

Suggest one change that is observed.   2

You must justify your answer.

[Turn over

MARKS | DO NOT WRITE IN THIS MARGIN

6.   **(continued)**

(c)   A student builds a model of a particle accelerator. The model accelerates a small ball on a circular track. A battery-operated motor accelerates the ball each time it passes the motor. To cause a collision a plastic block is pushed onto the track. The ball then hits the block.

plastic block   track   ball   motor

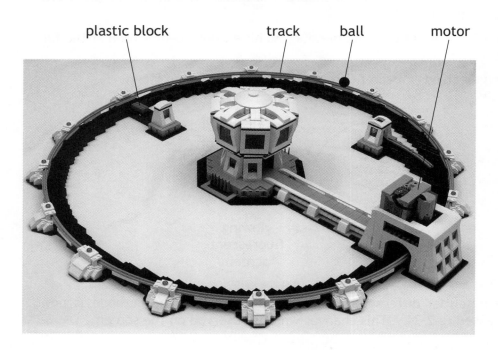

Using your knowledge of physics comment on the model compared to a real particle accelerator, such as the large hadron collider at CERN.

3

6. **(c)** **(continued)**

[Turn over

7. A student uses a gold-leaf electroscope to investigate the photoelectric effect. A deflection of the gold leaf on the electroscope shows that the metal plate is charged.

The student charges the metal plate on the electroscope and the gold leaf is deflected.

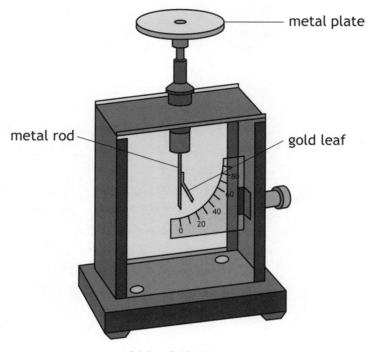

metal plate

metal rod

gold leaf

gold-leaf electroscope

(a) Ultraviolet light is shone onto the negatively charged metal plate. The gold-leaf electroscope does not discharge. This indicates that photoelectrons are not ejected from the surface of the metal.

Suggest one reason why photoelectrons are not ejected from the surface of the metal.

1

MARKS | DO NOT WRITE IN THIS MARGIN

7. **(continued)**

(b) The student adjusts the experiment so that the gold-leaf electroscope now discharges when ultraviolet light is shone onto the plate.

The work function for the metal plate is 6.94×10^{-19} J.

(i) State what is meant by a *work function of 6.94×10^{-19} J*.   **1**

(ii) The irradiance of the ultraviolet light on the metal plate is reduced by increasing the distance between the gold-leaf electroscope and the ultraviolet light source.

State what effect, if any, this has on the maximum kinetic energy of the photoelectrons ejected from the surface of the metal.   **2**

Justify your answer.

[Turn over

MARKS | DO NOT WRITE IN THIS MARGIN

7.   (continued)

(c)   The graph shows how the kinetic energy of the photoelectrons ejected from the metal plate varies as the frequency of the incident radiation increases.

The threshold frequency for the metal plate is $1 \cdot 05 \times 10^{15}$ Hz.

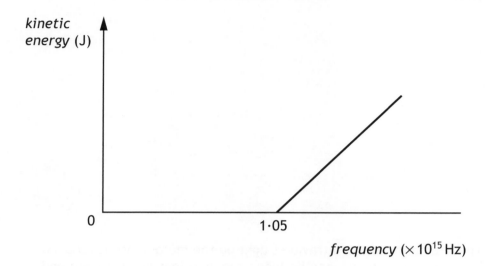

The metal plate is now replaced with a different metal plate made of aluminium.

The aluminium has a threshold frequency of $0 \cdot 99 \times 10^{15}$ Hz.

Add a line to the graph to show how the kinetic energy of the photoelectrons ejected from the aluminium plate varies as the frequency of the incident radiation increases.

2

(An additional graph, if required, can be found on *Page forty-five*.)

(d)   Explain why the photoelectric effect provides evidence for the particle nature of light.

1

MARKS | DO NOT WRITE IN THIS MARGIN

8. A student investigates interference of light by directing laser light of wavelength 630 nm onto a grating as shown.

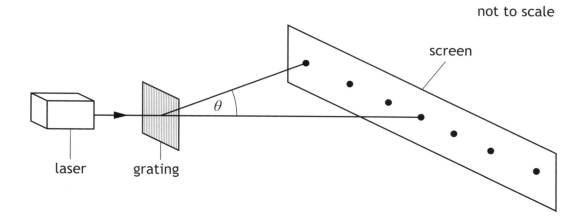

not to scale

(a) A pattern of bright spots is observed on a screen.

    (i) Explain, in terms of waves, how bright spots are produced on the screen.

1

    (ii) The grating has 250 lines per millimetre.

        Calculate the angle θ between the central maximum and the third order maximum.

3

        Space for working and answer

[Turn over

MARKS | DO NOT WRITE IN THIS MARGIN

8. (a) (continued)

(iii) The grating is now replaced by one which has 600 lines per millimetre.

State the effect of this change on the pattern observed. 2

Justify your answer.

(iv) The interference pattern is produced by coherent light.

State what is meant by the term *coherent*. 1

MARKS | DO NOT WRITE IN THIS MARGIN

8.   (continued)

(b)   The student now shines light from the laser onto a £5 note.

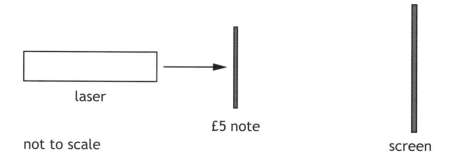

laser

£5 note

not to scale

screen

When it is shone through the transparent section of the note the student observes a pattern of bright spots on the screen.

The diagram below shows the pattern that the student observes on the screen.

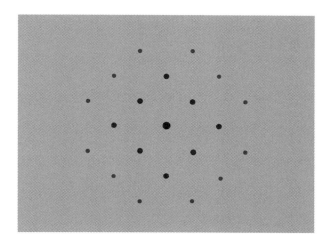

Suggest a reason for the difference in the pattern produced using the £5 note and the pattern produced using the grating.   1

[Turn over

MARKS | DO NOT WRITE IN THIS MARGIN

9. A ray of monochromatic light is incident on a glass prism as shown.

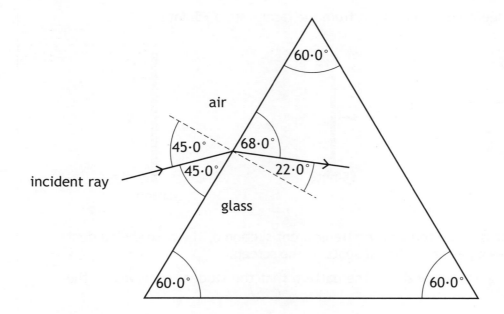

(a) Show that the refractive index of the glass for this ray of light is 1·89.   **2**

Space for working and answer

(b) (i) State what is meant by the term *critical angle*.   **1**

MARKS

9. (b) (continued)

    (ii) Calculate the critical angle for this light in the prism.

       Space for working and answer

3

    (iii) Complete the diagram below to show the path of the ray as it passes through the prism and emerges into the air.

       Mark on the diagram the values of all relevant angles.

4

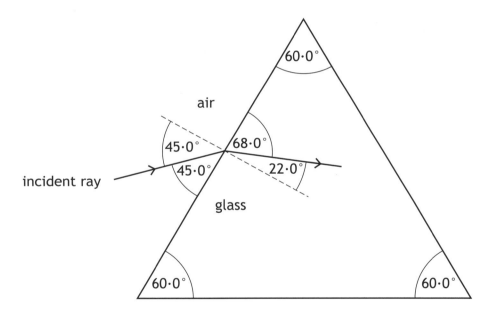

    (An additional diagram, if required, can be found on *Page forty-five*.)

[Turn over

MARKS | DO NOT WRITE IN THIS MARGIN

9. (continued)

(c) A ray of white light is shone through the prism and a spectrum is observed as shown.

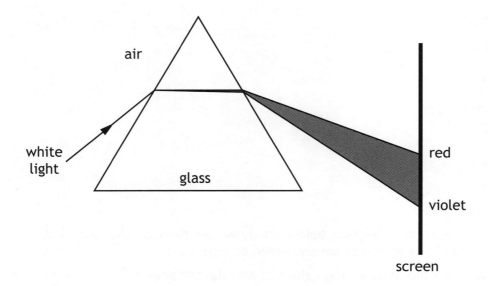

The prism is now replaced with another prism made from a different type of glass with a lower refractive index.

Describe one difference in the spectrum produced by this prism compared to the spectrum produced by the first prism.

1

MARKS | DO NOT WRITE IN THIS MARGIN

10.   In a laboratory experiment, light from a hydrogen discharge lamp is used to produce a line emission spectrum. The line spectrum for hydrogen has four lines in the visible region as shown.

(a)   The production of the line spectrum can be explained using the Bohr model of the atom.

State **two** features of the *Bohr model* of the atom.   2

[Turn over

MARKS | DO NOT WRITE IN THIS MARGIN

10.   (continued)

(b) Some of the energy levels of the hydrogen atom are shown.

E_4 ———————————— $-0 \cdot 871 \times 10^{-19}$ J

E_3 ———————————— $-1 \cdot 36 \times 10^{-19}$ J

E_2 ———————————— $-2 \cdot 42 \times 10^{-19}$ J

E_1 ———————————— $-5 \cdot 45 \times 10^{-19}$ J

E_0 ———————————— $-21 \cdot 8 \times 10^{-19}$ J

One of the spectral lines is due to electron transitions from E_3 to E_1.

Determine the frequency of the photon emitted when an electron makes this transition.

3

Space for working and answer

MARKS | DO NOT WRITE IN THIS MARGIN

10. **(continued)**

(c) In the laboratory, a line in the hydrogen spectrum is observed at a wavelength of 656 nm.

When the spectrum of light from a distant galaxy is viewed, this hydrogen line is now observed at a wavelength of 661 nm.

Determine the recessional velocity of the distant galaxy.   **5**

Space for working and answer

[Turn over

MARKS | DO NOT WRITE IN THIS MARGIN

11. A student constructs a battery using a potato, a strip of copper and a strip of magnesium.

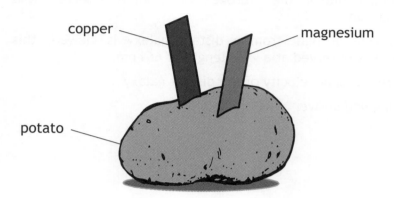

The student then sets up the following circuit with the potato battery connected to a variable resistor R, in order that the electromotive force (e.m.f.) and internal resistance of the battery may be determined.

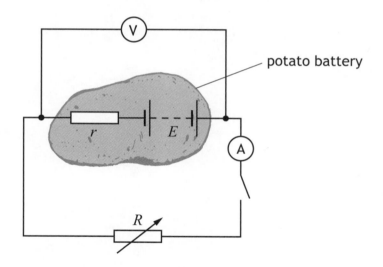

(a) State what is meant by the term *electromotive force* (e.m.f.).   1

MARKS | DO NOT WRITE IN THIS MARGIN

11. (continued)

(b) The student uses readings of current I and terminal potential difference V from this circuit to produce the graph shown.

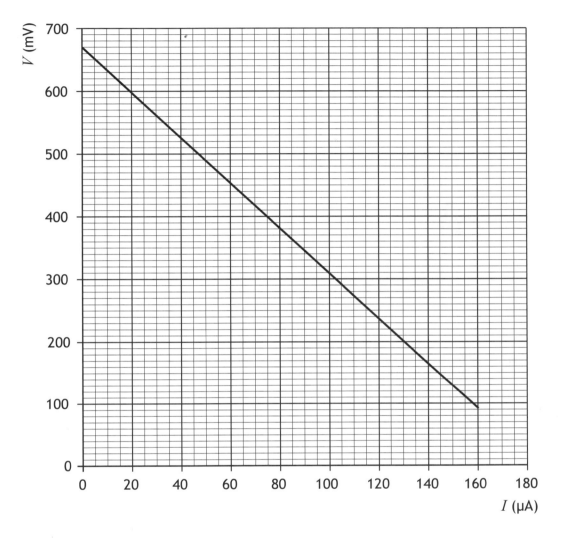

Determine the internal resistance of the potato battery.

3

Space for working and answer

[Turn over

11.   (continued)

(c)   The student connects a red LED and a blue LED, in turn, to the battery.

The LEDs are forward biased when connected.

The student observes that the battery will operate the red LED but not the blue LED.

The diagram represents the band structure of the blue LED.

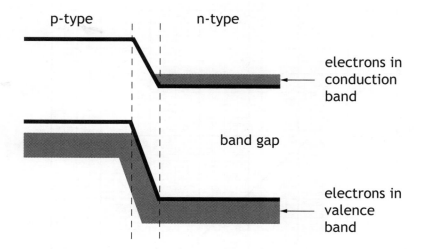

LEDs emit light when electrons fall from the conduction band into the valence band of the p-type semiconductor.

Explain, using **band theory**, why the blue LED will not operate with this battery.

1

[Turn over for next question

DO NOT WRITE ON THIS PAGE

12. A student carries out a series of experiments to investigate alternating current.

(a) A signal generator is connected to an oscilloscope and a circuit as shown.

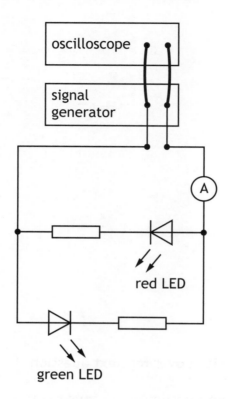

The output of the signal generator is displayed on the oscilloscope.

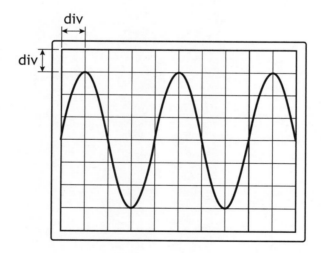

The Y-gain setting on the oscilloscope is 1·0 V/div.

The timebase setting on the oscilloscope is 0·5 s/div.

MARKS | DO NOT WRITE IN THIS MARGIN

12. (a) (continued)

(i) Determine the peak voltage of the output of the signal generator.   **1**

Space for working and answer

(ii) Determine the frequency of the output of the signal generator.   **3**

Space for working and answer

(iii) The student observes that the red LED is only lit when the ammeter gives a positive reading and the green LED is only lit when the ammeter gives a negative reading.

Explain these observations.   **2**

12.   **(continued)**

(b)   The signal generator is now connected in a circuit as shown.

The settings on the signal generator are unchanged.

The signal generator has negligible internal resistance.

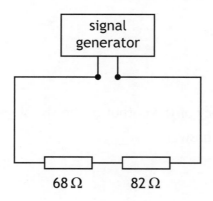

Determine the r.m.s. voltage across the 82 Ω resistor.   **5**

Space for working and answer

MARKS | DO NOT WRITE IN THIS MARGIN

13. A student sets up an experiment to investigate the pressure due to a liquid as shown.

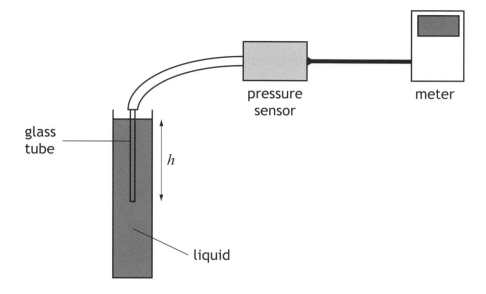

The pressure due to a liquid is given by the relationship

$$p = \rho g h$$

where p is the pressure due to the liquid in pascals (Pa),

g is the gravitational field strength in N kg^{-1},

ρ is the density of the liquid in kg m^{-3},

and h is the depth in the liquid in m.

(a) The student initially carries out the investigation using water.

The density of water is $1{\cdot}00 \times 10^3$ kg m^{-3}.

Calculate the pressure due to the water at a depth of $0{\cdot}35$ m.   2

Space for working and answer

13. **(continued)**

(b) The student repeats the experiment with a different liquid.

The pressure meter is set to zero before the glass tube is lowered into the liquid.

The student takes measurements of the pressure at various depths below the surface of the liquid.

The student records the following information.

Depth, h (m)	Pressure, p (kPa)
0·10	1·2
0·20	2·5
0·30	3·6
0·40	4·9
0·50	6·2

(i) Using the square-ruled paper on *Page forty-three*, draw a graph of p against h. **3**

(Additional graph paper, if required, can be found on *Page forty-four*.)

(ii) Calculate the gradient of your graph. **2**

Space for working and answer

(iii) Determine the density of this liquid. **2**

Space for working and answer

[END OF QUESTION PAPER]

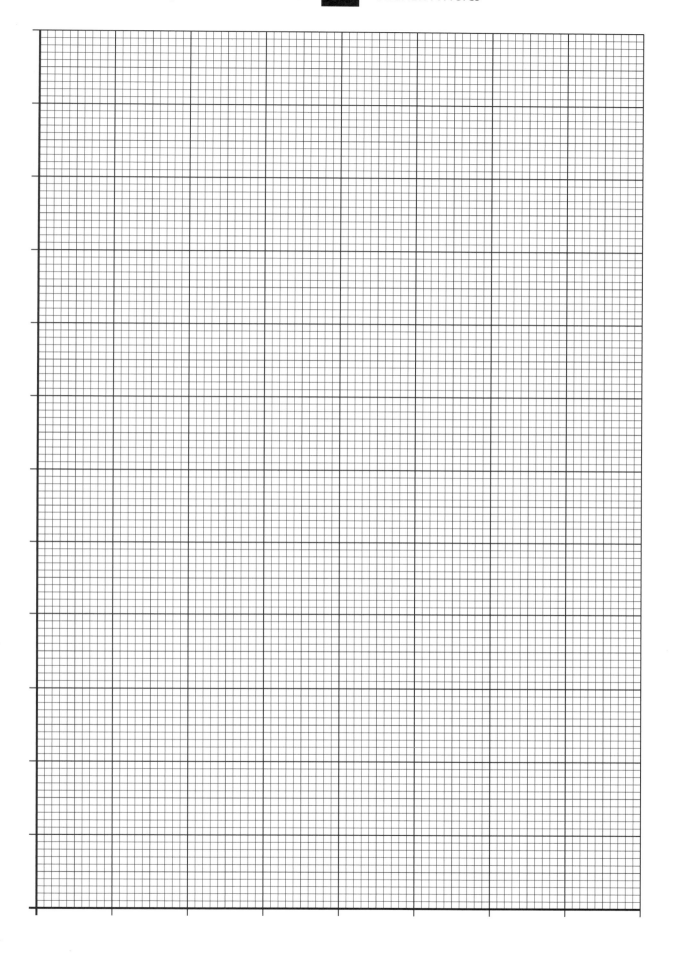

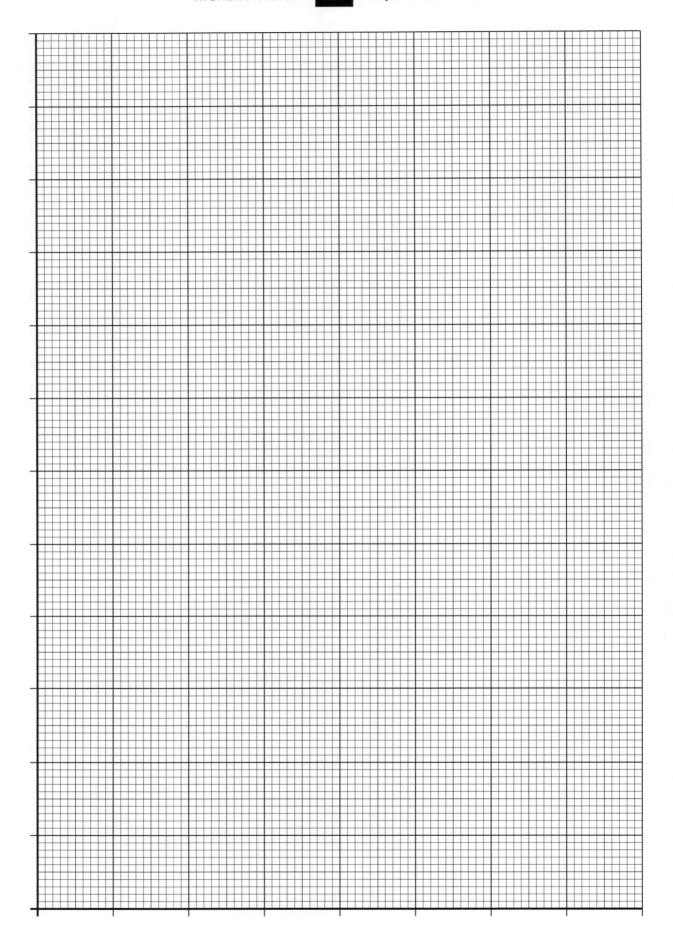

MARKS | DO NOT WRITE IN THIS MARGIN

ADDITIONAL SPACE FOR ANSWERS AND ROUGH WORK

Additional graph for use with Question 7 (c)

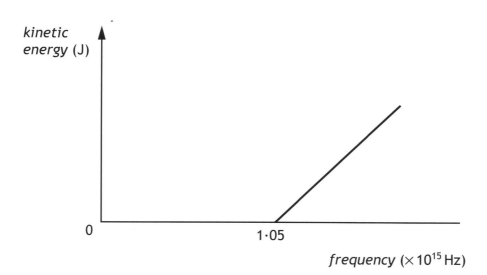

Additional diagram for use with Question 9 (b) (iii)

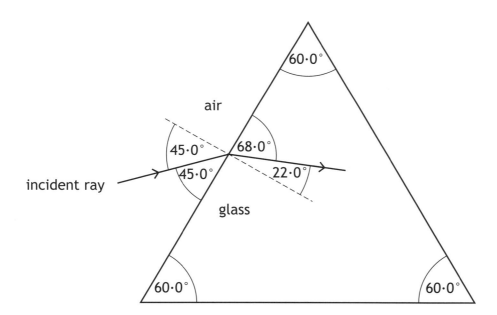

ADDITIONAL SPACE FOR ANSWERS AND ROUGH WORK

MARKS | DO NOT WRITE IN THIS MARGIN

ADDITIONAL SPACE FOR ANSWERS AND ROUGH WORK

MARKS | DO NOT WRITE IN THIS MARGIN

[BLANK PAGE]

DO NOT WRITE ON THIS PAGE

HIGHER

2018 Specimen Question Paper

National
Qualifications
SPECIMEN ONLY

S857/76/12

Physics
Paper 1 — Multiple choice

Date — Not applicable

Duration — 45 minutes

Total marks — 25

Attempt ALL questions.

You may use a calculator.

Instructions for the completion of Paper 1 are given on *page two* of your answer booklet S857/76/02.

Record your answers on the answer grid on *page three* of your answer booklet.

Reference may be made to the data sheet on *page two* of this question paper and to the relationships sheet S857/76/22.

Space for rough work is provided at the end of this booklet.

Before leaving the examination room you must give your answer booklet to the Invigilator; if you do not, you may lose all the marks for this paper.

DATA SHEET

COMMON PHYSICAL QUANTITIES

Quantity	Symbol	Value	Quantity	Symbol	Value
Speed of light in vacuum	c	$3 \cdot 00 \times 10^8 \, \mathrm{m\,s^{-1}}$	Planck's constant	h	$6 \cdot 63 \times 10^{-34} \, \mathrm{J\,s}$
Magnitude of the charge on an electron	e	$1 \cdot 60 \times 10^{-19} \, \mathrm{C}$	Mass of electron	m_e	$9 \cdot 11 \times 10^{-31} \, \mathrm{kg}$
Universal Constant of Gravitation	G	$6 \cdot 67 \times 10^{-11} \, \mathrm{m^3\,kg^{-1}\,s^{-2}}$	Mass of neutron	m_n	$1 \cdot 675 \times 10^{-27} \, \mathrm{kg}$
Gravitational acceleration on Earth	g	$9 \cdot 8 \, \mathrm{m\,s^{-2}}$	Mass of proton	m_p	$1 \cdot 673 \times 10^{-27} \, \mathrm{kg}$
Hubble's constant	H_0	$2 \cdot 3 \times 10^{-18} \, \mathrm{s^{-1}}$			

REFRACTIVE INDICES

The refractive indices refer to sodium light of wavelength 589 nm and to substances at a temperature of 273 K.

Substance	Refractive index	Substance	Refractive index
Diamond	2·42	Water	1·33
Crown glass	1·50	Air	1·00

SPECTRAL LINES

Element	Wavelength/nm	Colour	Element	Wavelength/nm	Colour
Hydrogen	656	Red	Cadmium	644	Red
	486	Blue-green		509	Green
	434	Blue-violet		480	Blue
	410	Violet	Lasers		
	397	Ultraviolet	Element	Wavelength/nm	Colour
	389	Ultraviolet	Carbon dioxide	9550 ⎫ 10590 ⎬	Infrared
Sodium	589	Yellow	Helium-neon	633	Red

PROPERTIES OF SELECTED MATERIALS

Substance	Density/kg m^{-3}	Melting point/K	Boiling point/K
Aluminium	$2 \cdot 70 \times 10^3$	933	2623
Copper	$8 \cdot 96 \times 10^3$	1357	2853
Ice	$9 \cdot 20 \times 10^2$	273	. . . .
Sea Water	$1 \cdot 02 \times 10^3$	264	377
Water	$1 \cdot 00 \times 10^3$	273	373
Air	1·29	. . . .	. . . .
Hydrogen	$9 \cdot 0 \times 10^{-2}$	14	20

The gas densities refer to a temperature of 273 K and a pressure of $1 \cdot 01 \times 10^5$ Pa.

Total marks — 25

Attempt ALL questions

1. The following velocity-time graph represents the vertical motion of a ball.

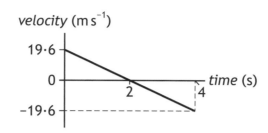

Which of the following acceleration-time graphs represents the same motion?

A

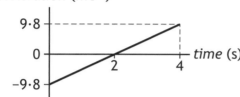

B

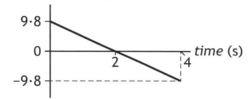

C

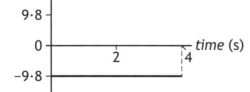

D

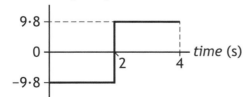

E

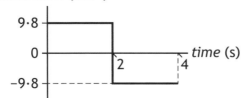

[Turn over

2. A train accelerates uniformly from $5 \cdot 0 \, m \, s^{-1}$ to $12 \cdot 0 \, m \, s^{-1}$ while travelling a distance of 119 m along a straight track.

   The acceleration of the train is

   A $0 \cdot 50 \, m \, s^{-2}$

   B $0 \cdot 70 \, m \, s^{-2}$

   C $1 \cdot 2 \, m \, s^{-2}$

   D $7 \cdot 0 \, m \, s^{-2}$

   E $14 \, m \, s^{-2}$.

3. Two blocks are linked by a newton balance of negligible mass.

   The blocks are placed on a level, frictionless surface. A force of 18·0 N is applied to the blocks as shown.

   The reading on the newton balance is

   A   3·6 N

   B   7·2 N

   C   9·0 N

   D   10·8 N

   E   18·0 N.

4. A block of wood slides with a constant velocity down a slope. The slope makes an angle of 30·0° with the horizontal as shown. The mass of the block is 2·0 kg.

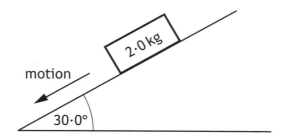

The magnitude of the force of friction acting on the block is

A   1·0 N

B   1·7 N

C   9·8 N

D   17 N

E   19·6 N.

5. The diagram shows the masses and velocities of two trolleys just before they collide on a level bench.

After the collision, the trolleys move along the bench joined together.

The kinetic energy lost in this collision is

A   0 J

B   6·0 J

C   12 J

D   18 J

E   24 J.

[Turn over

6. The graph shows the force which acts on an object over a time interval of 8·0 seconds.

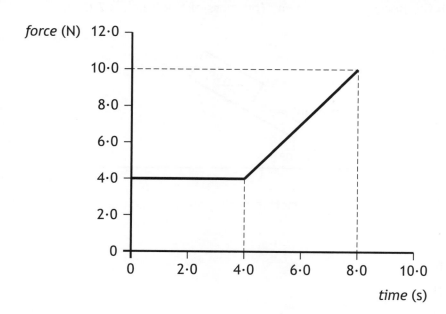

The momentum gained by the object during the 8·0 seconds is

A $12 \, kg \, m \, s^{-1}$

B $32 \, kg \, m \, s^{-1}$

C $44 \, kg \, m \, s^{-1}$

D $52 \, kg \, m \, s^{-1}$

E $80 \, kg \, m \, s^{-1}$.

7. A javelin is thrown at an angle of 60·0° to the horizontal with a speed of $20·0 \, m \, s^{-1}$.

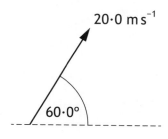

The javelin is in flight for 3·50 s.

The effects of air resistance can be ignored.

The horizontal distance travelled by the javelin is

A   15·3 m

B   35·0 m

C   60·6 m

D   70·0 m

E   121 m.

-->

8. Two small asteroids are 12 m apart.

    The masses of the asteroids are 2.0×10^3 kg and 0.050×10^3 kg.

    The gravitational force acting between the asteroids is

    A 1.2×10^{-9} N

    B 4.6×10^{-8} N

    C 5.6×10^{-7} N

    D 1.9×10^{-6} N

    E 6.8×10^{3} N.

9. A spaceship on a launch pad is measured to have a length L.

    This spaceship has a speed of 2.5×10^8 m s^{-1} as it passes a planet.

    Which row in the table describes the length of the spaceship as measured by the pilot in the spaceship and an observer on the planet?

	Length measured by pilot in the spaceship	Length measured by observer on the planet
A	L	greater than L
B	L	L
C	L	less than L
D	greater than L	L
E	less than L	less than L

[Turn over

10. The siren on an ambulance is emitting sound with a constant frequency of 900 Hz. The ambulance is travelling at a constant speed of $25\,\mathrm{m\,s^{-1}}$ as it approaches and passes a stationary observer. The speed of sound in air is $340\,\mathrm{m\,s^{-1}}$.

Which row in the table shows the frequency of the sound heard by the observer as the ambulance approaches and as it moves away from the observer?

	Frequency as ambulance approaches (Hz)	Frequency as ambulance moves away (Hz)
A	900	838
B	971	838
C	838	900
D	971	900
E	838	971

11. Cosmic microwave background radiation and Olbers' paradox provide evidence for

A the photoelectric effect

B the Bohr model of the atom

C the theory of special relativity

D the Big Bang theory

E Newton's Law of Universal Gravitation.

12. A student makes the following statements about particles in electric fields.

I A neutron experiences a force in an electric field.

II When an alpha particle is moved in an electric field work is done.

III An electric field applied to a conductor causes the free electrons in the conductor to move.

Which of the statements is/are correct?

A II only

B III only

C I and II only

D II and III only

E I, II and III

13. The electric field patterns around charged particles Q, R and S are shown.

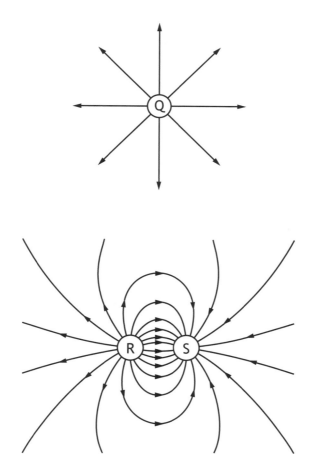

Which row in the table shows the charges on particles Q, R and S?

	Charge on Q	Charge on R	Charge on S
A	negative	negative	positive
B	positive	positive	negative
C	negative	positive	negative
D	negative	negative	negative
E	positive	positive	positive

[Turn over

14. A student makes the following statements about an electron.

   I   An electron is a boson.

   II   An electron is a lepton.

   III An electron is a fermion.

   Which of these statements is/are correct?

   A   I only

   B   II only

   C   III only

   D   I and II only

   E   II and III only

15. The last two changes in a radioactive decay series are shown below.

   A Bismuth nucleus emits a beta particle and its product, a Polonium nucleus, emits an alpha particle.

$$_{Q}^{P}\text{Bi} \xrightarrow[\text{decay}]{\beta} {_{S}^{R}\text{Po}} \xrightarrow[\text{decay}]{\alpha} {_{82}^{208}\text{Pb}}$$

   Which numbers are represented by P, Q, R and S?

	P	Q	R	S
A	210	83	208	81
B	210	83	210	84
C	211	85	207	86
D	212	83	212	84
E	212	85	212	84

16. Light from a point source is incident on a screen. The screen is $3 \cdot 0$ m from the source. The irradiance at the screen is $8 \cdot 0$ W m^{-2}.

The light source is now moved to a distance of 12 m from the screen.

The irradiance at the screen is now

A $0 \cdot 50$ W m^{-2}

B $2 \cdot 0$ W m^{-2}

C $4 \cdot 0$ W m^{-2}

D $6 \cdot 0$ W m^{-2}

E $8 \cdot 0$ W m^{-2}.

17. S_1 and S_2 are sources of coherent waves.

An interference pattern is obtained between X and Y.

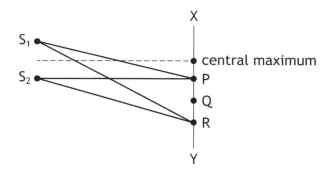

The first order maximum occurs at P, where $S_1P = 200$ mm and $S_2P = 180$ mm.

For the third order maximum, at R, the path difference $(S_1R - S_2R)$ is

A   20 mm

B   30 mm

C   40 mm

D   50 mm

E   60 mm.

[Turn over

18. In an atom, a photon is emitted when an electron makes a transition from a higher energy level to a lower energy level as shown.

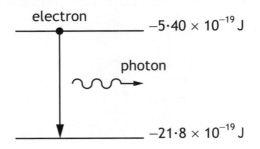

electron $-5 \cdot 40 \times 10^{-19}$ J

photon

$-21 \cdot 8 \times 10^{-19}$ J

The wavelength of the radiation emitted due to an electron transition between the two energy levels shown is

A $7 \cdot 31 \times 10^{-8}$ m

B $9 \cdot 12 \times 10^{-8}$ m

C $1 \cdot 21 \times 10^{-7}$ m

D $8 \cdot 23 \times 10^{6}$ m

E $2 \cdot 47 \times 10^{15}$ m.

19. A ray of red light travels from air into water.

Which row in the table describes the change, if any, in speed and frequency of a ray of red light as it travels from air into water?

	Speed	*Frequency*
A	stays constant	decreases
B	increases	increases
C	increases	stays constant
D	decreases	stays constant
E	decreases	decreases

20. The rms voltage of the mains supply is 230 V.

The approximate value of the peak voltage is

A   115 V

B   163 V

C   325 V

D   460 V

E   651 V.

21. An oscilloscope is connected to the output terminals of a signal generator.

The trace displayed on the screen is shown.

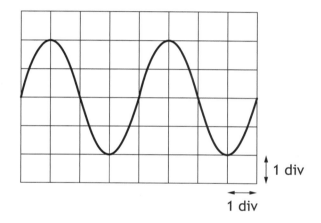

The timebase of the oscilloscope is set at 30 ms/div.

The frequency of the output signal from the signal generator is

A 4.2×10^{-3} Hz

B 8.3×10^{-3} Hz

C   0.12 Hz

D   4.2 Hz

E   8.3 Hz.

[Turn over

22. In the diagrams below, each resistor has the same resistance.

    Which combination has the least value of the effective resistance between the terminals X and Y?

    A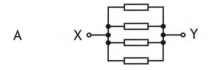

    B

    C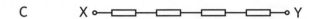

    D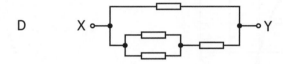

    E

23. Four resistors each of resistance $20\,\Omega$ are connected to a $60\,V$ supply of negligible internal resistance as shown.

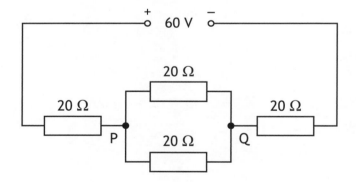

The potential difference across PQ is

A $12\,V$

B $15\,V$

C $20\,V$

D $24\,V$

E $30\,V$.

24. The EMF of a battery is

A   the total energy supplied by the battery

B   the voltage lost due to the internal resistance of the battery

C   the total charge which passes through the battery

D   the number of coulombs of charge passing through the battery per second

E   the energy supplied to each coulomb of charge passing through the battery.

25. A student carries out three experiments to investigate the charging of a capacitor using a DC supply.

The graphs obtained from the experiments are shown.

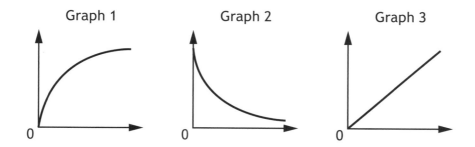

The axes of the graphs have not been labelled.

Which row in the table shows the labels for the axes of the graphs?

	Graph 1	Graph 2	Graph 3
A	voltage and time	charge and voltage	current and time
B	current and time	voltage and time	charge and voltage
C	current and time	charge and voltage	voltage and time
D	voltage and time	current and time	charge and voltage
E	charge and voltage	current and time	voltage and time

[END OF SPECIMEN QUESTION PAPER]

SPACE FOR ROUGH WORK

SPACE FOR ROUGH WORK

National
Qualifications
SPECIMEN ONLY

S857/76/22

Physics
Paper 1 — Relationships sheet

Date — Not applicable

Relationships required for Physics Higher

$d = \bar{v}t$

$s = \bar{v}t$

$v = u + at$

$s = ut + \frac{1}{2}at^2$

$v^2 = u^2 + 2as$

$s = \frac{1}{2}(u+v)t$

$F = ma$

$W = mg$

$E_w = Fd, \text{ or } W = Fd$

$E_p = mgh$

$E_k = \frac{1}{2}mv^2$

$P = \dfrac{E}{t}$

$p = mv$

$Ft = mv - mu$

$F = G\dfrac{m_1 m_2}{r^2}$

$t' = \dfrac{t}{\sqrt{1 - \left(\dfrac{v}{c}\right)^2}}$

$l' = l\sqrt{1 - \left(\dfrac{v}{c}\right)^2}$

$f_o = f_s\left(\dfrac{v}{v \pm v_s}\right)$

$z = \dfrac{\lambda_{observed} - \lambda_{rest}}{\lambda_{rest}}$

$z = \dfrac{v}{c}$

$v = H_0 d$

$W = QV$

$E = mc^2$

$I = \dfrac{P}{A}$

$I = \dfrac{k}{d^2}$

$I_1 d_1^2 = I_2 d_2^2$

$E = hf$

$E_k = hf - hf_0$

$v = f\lambda$

$E_2 - E_1 = hf$

$d \sin\theta = m\lambda$

$n = \dfrac{\sin\theta_1}{\sin\theta_2}$

$\dfrac{\sin\theta_1}{\sin\theta_2} = \dfrac{\lambda_1}{\lambda_2} = \dfrac{v_1}{v_2}$

$\sin\theta_c = \dfrac{1}{n}$

$V_{rms} = \dfrac{V_{peak}}{\sqrt{2}}$

$I_{rms} = \dfrac{I_{peak}}{\sqrt{2}}$

$T = \dfrac{1}{f}$

$V = IR$

$P = IV = I^2 R = \dfrac{V^2}{R}$

$R_T = R_1 + R_2 + ...$

$\dfrac{1}{R_T} = \dfrac{1}{R_1} + \dfrac{1}{R_2} + ...$

$V_1 = \left(\dfrac{R_1}{R_1 + R_2}\right)V_s$

$\dfrac{V_1}{V_2} = \dfrac{R_1}{R_2}$

$E = V + Ir$

$C = \dfrac{Q}{V}$

$Q = It$

$E = \frac{1}{2}QV = \frac{1}{2}CV^2 = \frac{1}{2}\dfrac{Q^2}{C}$

path difference $= m\lambda$ or $\left(m + \frac{1}{2}\right)\lambda$ where $m = 0, 1, 2...$

random uncertainty $= \dfrac{max.\,value - min.\,value}{number\,of\,values}$

or

$\Delta R = \dfrac{R_{max} - R_{min}}{n}$

Additional relationships

Circle

circumference $= 2\pi r$

area $= \pi r^2$

Sphere

area $= 4\pi r^2$

volume $= \frac{4}{3}\pi r^3$

Trigonometry

$\sin \theta = \dfrac{\text{opposite}}{\text{hypotenuse}}$

$\cos \theta = \dfrac{\text{adjacent}}{\text{hypotenuse}}$

$\tan \theta = \dfrac{\text{opposite}}{\text{adjacent}}$

$\sin^2 \theta + \cos^2 \theta = 1$

Electron arrangements of elements

Key

Atomic number
Symbol
Electron arrangement
Name

Main groups and transition elements

Format: Atomic number — Symbol — Electron arrangement — Name

Group 1 (1)

No.	Symbol	Electron arrangement	Name
1	H	(1)	Hydrogen
3	Li	2,1	Lithium
11	Na	2,8,1	Sodium
19	K	2,8,8,1	Potassium
37	Rb	2,8,18,8,1	Rubidium
55	Cs	2,8,18,18,8,1	Caesium
87	Fr	2,8,18,32,18,8,1	Francium

Group 2 (2)

No.	Symbol	Electron arrangement	Name
4	Be	2,2	Beryllium
12	Mg	2,8,2	Magnesium
20	Ca	2,8,8,2	Calcium
38	Sr	2,8,18,8,2	Strontium
56	Ba	2,8,18,18,8,2	Barium
88	Ra	2,8,18,32,18,8,2	Radium

Transition elements

No.	Symbol	Electron arrangement	Name	Column
21	Sc	2,8,9,2	Scandium	(3)
39	Y	2,8,18,9,2	Yttrium	(3)
57	La	2,8,18,18,9,2	Lanthanum	(3)
89	Ac	2,8,18,32,18,9,2	Actinium	(3)
22	Ti	2,8,10,2	Titanium	(4)
40	Zr	2,8,18,10,2	Zirconium	(4)
72	Hf	2,8,18,32,10,2	Hafnium	(4)
104	Rf	2,8,18,32,32,10,2	Rutherfordium	(4)
23	V	2,8,11,2	Vanadium	(5)
41	Nb	2,8,18,12,1	Niobium	(5)
73	Ta	2,8,18,32,11,2	Tantalum	(5)
105	Db	2,8,18,32,32,11,2	Dubnium	(5)
24	Cr	2,8,13,1	Chromium	(6)
42	Mo	2,8,18,13,1	Molybdenum	(6)
74	W	2,8,18,32,12,2	Tungsten	(6)
106	Sg	2,8,18,32,32,12,2	Seaborgium	(6)
25	Mn	2,8,13,2	Manganese	(7)
43	Tc	2,8,18,13,2	Technetium	(7)
75	Re	2,8,18,32,13,2	Rhenium	(7)
107	Bh	2,8,18,32,32,13,2	Bohrium	(7)
26	Fe	2,8,14,2	Iron	(8)
44	Ru	2,8,18,15,1	Ruthenium	(8)
76	Os	2,8,18,32,14,2	Osmium	(8)
108	Hs	2,8,18,32,32,14,2	Hassium	(8)
27	Co	2,8,15,2	Cobalt	(9)
45	Rh	2,8,18,16,1	Rhodium	(9)
77	Ir	2,8,18,32,15,2	Iridium	(9)
109	Mt	2,8,18,32,32,15,2	Meitnerium	(9)
28	Ni	2,8,16,2	Nickel	(10)
46	Pd	2,8,18,18,0	Palladium	(10)
78	Pt	2,8,18,32,17,1	Platinum	(10)
110	Ds	2,8,18,32,32,17,1	Darmstadtium	(10)
29	Cu	2,8,18,1	Copper	(11)
47	Ag	2,8,18,18,1	Silver	(11)
79	Au	2,8,18,32,18,1	Gold	(11)
111	Rg	2,8,18,32,32,18,1	Roentgenium	(11)
30	Zn	2,8,18,2	Zinc	(12)
48	Cd	2,8,18,18,2	Cadmium	(12)
80	Hg	2,8,18,32,18,2	Mercury	(12)
112	Cn	2,8,18,32,32,18,2	Copernicium	(12)

Group 3 (13)

No.	Symbol	Electron arrangement	Name
5	B	2,3	Boron
13	Al	2,8,3	Aluminium
31	Ga	2,8,18,3	Gallium
49	In	2,8,18,18,3	Indium
81	Tl	2,8,18,32,18,3	Thallium

Group 4 (14)

No.	Symbol	Electron arrangement	Name
6	C	2,4	Carbon
14	Si	2,8,4	Silicon
32	Ge	2,8,18,4	Germanium
50	Sn	2,8,18,18,4	Tin
82	Pb	2,8,18,32,18,4	Lead

Group 5 (15)

No.	Symbol	Electron arrangement	Name
7	N	2,5	Nitrogen
15	P	2,8,5	Phosphorus
33	As	2,8,18,5	Arsenic
51	Sb	2,8,18,18,5	Antimony
83	Bi	2,8,18,32,18,5	Bismuth

Group 6 (16)

No.	Symbol	Electron arrangement	Name
8	O	2,6	Oxygen
16	S	2,8,6	Sulfur
34	Se	2,8,18,6	Selenium
52	Te	2,8,18,18,6	Tellurium
84	Po	2,8,18,32,18,6	Polonium

Group 7 (17)

No.	Symbol	Electron arrangement	Name
9	F	2,7	Fluorine
17	Cl	2,8,7	Chlorine
35	Br	2,8,18,7	Bromine
53	I	2,8,18,18,7	Iodine
85	At	2,8,18,32,18,7	Astatine

Group 0 (18)

No.	Symbol	Electron arrangement	Name
2	He	2	Helium
10	Ne	2,8	Neon
18	Ar	2,8,8	Argon
36	Kr	2,8,18,8	Krypton
54	Xe	2,8,18,18,8	Xenon
86	Rn	2,8,18,32,18,8	Radon

Lanthanides

No.	Symbol	Electron arrangement	Name
57	La	2,8,18,18,9,2	Lanthanum
58	Ce	2,8,18,20,8,2	Cerium
59	Pr	2,8,18,21,8,2	Praseodymium
60	Nd	2,8,18,22,8,2	Neodymium
61	Pm	2,8,18,23,8,2	Promethium
62	Sm	2,8,18,24,8,2	Samarium
63	Eu	2,8,18,25,8,2	Europium
64	Gd	2,8,18,25,9,2	Gadolinium
65	Tb	2,8,18,27,8,2	Terbium
66	Dy	2,8,18,28,8,2	Dysprosium
67	Ho	2,8,18,29,8,2	Holmium
68	Er	2,8,18,30,8,2	Erbium
69	Tm	2,8,18,31,8,2	Thulium
70	Yb	2,8,18,32,8,2	Ytterbium
71	Lu	2,8,18,32,9,2	Lutetium

Actinides

No.	Symbol	Electron arrangement	Name
89	Ac	2,8,18,32,18,9,2	Actinium
90	Th	2,8,18,32,18,10,2	Thorium
91	Pa	2,8,18,32,20,9,2	Protactinium
92	U	2,8,18,32,21,9,2	Uranium
93	Np	2,8,18,32,22,9,2	Neptunium
94	Pu	2,8,18,32,24,8,2	Plutonium
95	Am	2,8,18,32,25,8,2	Americium
96	Cm	2,8,18,32,25,9,2	Curium
97	Bk	2,8,18,32,27,8,2	Berkelium
98	Cf	2,8,18,32,28,8,2	Californium
99	Es	2,8,18,32,29,8,2	Einsteinium
100	Fm	2,8,18,32,30,8,2	Fermium
101	Md	2,8,18,32,31,8,2	Mendelevium
102	No	2,8,18,32,32,8,2	Nobelium
103	Lr	2,8,18,32,32,9,2	Lawrencium

H National Qualifications
SPECIMEN ONLY

Mark

S857/76/02

Physics
Paper 1 — Multiple choice
Answer booklet

Date — Not applicable

Duration — 45 minutes

Fill in these boxes and read what is printed below.

Full name of centre

Town

Forename(s)

Surname

Number of seat

Date of birth

Day	Month	Year

Scottish candidate number

Instructions for the completion of Paper 1 are given on *page two*.

Record your answers on the answer grid on *page three*.

Use **blue** or **black** ink.

Before leaving the examination room you must give your answer booklet to the Invigilator; if you do not, you may lose all the marks for this paper.

The questions for Paper 1 are contained in the question paper S857/76/12.

Read these and record your answers on the answer grid on *page three*.

Use **blue** or **black** ink. Do NOT use gel pens or pencil.

1. The answer to each question is **either** A, B, C, D or E. Decide what your answer is, then fill in the appropriate bubble (see sample question below).

2. There is **only one correct** answer to each question.

3. Any rough working should be done on the space for rough work at the end of the question paper S857/76/12.

Sample question

The energy unit measured by the electricity meter in your home is the

    A   ampere

    B   kilowatt-hour

    C   watt

    D   coulomb

    E   volt.

The correct answer is **B** — kilowatt-hour. The answer **B** bubble has been clearly filled in (see below).

Changing an answer

If you decide to change your answer, cancel your first answer by putting a cross through it (see below) and fill in the answer you want. The answer below has been changed to **D**.

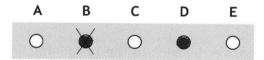

If you then decide to change back to an answer you have already scored out, put a tick (✓) to the **right** of the answer you want, as shown below:

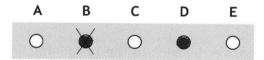

SECTION 1 — Answer Grid

	A	B	C	D	E
1	○	○	○	○	○
2	○	○	○	○	○
3	○	○	○	○	○
4	○	○	○	○	○
5	○	○	○	○	○
6	○	○	○	○	○
7	○	○	○	○	○
8	○	○	○	○	○
9	○	○	○	○	○
10	○	○	○	○	○
11	○	○	○	○	○
12	○	○	○	○	○
13	○	○	○	○	○
14	○	○	○	○	○
15	○	○	○	○	○
16	○	○	○	○	○
17	○	○	○	○	○
18	○	○	○	○	○
19	○	○	○	○	○
20	○	○	○	○	○
21	○	○	○	○	○
22	○	○	○	○	○
23	○	○	○	○	○
24	○	○	○	○	○
25	○	○	○	○	○

National
Qualifications
SPECIMEN ONLY

Mark

S857/76/01

**Physics
Paper 2**

Date — Not applicable

Duration — 2 hours 15 minutes

Fill in these boxes and read what is printed below.

Full name of centre

Town

Forename(s)

Surname

Number of seat

Date of birth

Day	Month	Year

Scottish candidate number

Total marks — 130

Attempt ALL questions.

You may use a calculator.

Reference may be made to the data sheet on *page two* of this booklet and to the relationships sheet S857/76/11.

Care should be taken to give an appropriate number of significant figures in the final answers to calculations.

Write your answers clearly in the spaces provided in this booklet. Additional space for answers and rough work is provided at the end of this booklet. If you use this space you must clearly identify the question number you are attempting. Any rough work must be written in this booklet. Score through your rough work when you have written your final copy.

Use **blue** or **black** ink.

Before leaving the examination room you must give this booklet to the Invigilator; if you do not, you may lose all the marks for this paper.

DATA SHEET

COMMON PHYSICAL QUANTITIES

Quantity	Symbol	Value	Quantity	Symbol	Value
Speed of light in vacuum	c	$3 \cdot 00 \times 10^8 \, m \, s^{-1}$	Planck's constant	h	$6 \cdot 63 \times 10^{-34} \, J \, s$
Magnitude of the charge on an electron	e	$1 \cdot 60 \times 10^{-19} \, C$	Mass of electron	m_e	$9 \cdot 11 \times 10^{-31} \, kg$
Universal Constant of Gravitation	G	$6 \cdot 67 \times 10^{-11} \, m^3 \, kg^{-1} \, s^{-2}$	Mass of neutron	m_n	$1 \cdot 675 \times 10^{-27} \, kg$
Gravitational acceleration on Earth	g	$9 \cdot 8 \, m \, s^{-2}$	Mass of proton	m_p	$1 \cdot 673 \times 10^{-27} \, kg$
Hubble's constant	H_0	$2 \cdot 3 \times 10^{-18} \, s^{-1}$			

REFRACTIVE INDICES

The refractive indices refer to sodium light of wavelength 589 nm and to substances at a temperature of 273 K.

Substance	Refractive index	Substance	Refractive index
Diamond	2·42	Water	1·33
Crown glass	1·50	Air	1·00

SPECTRAL LINES

Element	Wavelength/nm	Colour	Element	Wavelength/nm	Colour
Hydrogen	656	Red	Cadmium	644	Red
	486	Blue-green		509	Green
	434	Blue-violet		480	Blue
	410	Violet		Lasers	
	397	Ultraviolet	Element	Wavelength/nm	Colour
	389	Ultraviolet	Carbon dioxide	9550 } 10590 }	Infrared
Sodium	589	Yellow	Helium-neon	633	Red

PROPERTIES OF SELECTED MATERIALS

Substance	Density/kg m^{-3}	Melting point/K	Boiling point/K
Aluminium	$2 \cdot 70 \times 10^3$	933	2623
Copper	$8 \cdot 96 \times 10^3$	1357	2853
Ice	$9 \cdot 20 \times 10^2$	273	. . . .
Sea Water	$1 \cdot 02 \times 10^3$	264	377
Water	$1 \cdot 00 \times 10^3$	273	373
Air	1·29	. . . .	. . . .
Hydrogen	$9 \cdot 0 \times 10^{-2}$	14	20

The gas densities refer to a temperature of 273 K and a pressure of $1 \cdot 01 \times 10^5$ Pa.

MARKS | DO NOT WRITE IN THIS MARGIN

Total marks — 130

Attempt ALL questions

1. A car is travelling at a constant speed of $15 \cdot 0 \, \text{m s}^{-1}$ along a straight, level road.

   It passes a motorcycle which is stationary at the roadside.

   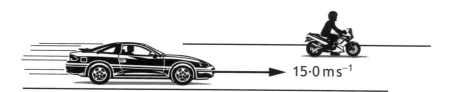

   $15 \cdot 0 \, \text{m s}^{-1}$

   At the instant the car passes, the motorcycle starts to move in the same direction as the car.

   The graph shows the motion of each vehicle from the instant the car passes the motorcycle.

   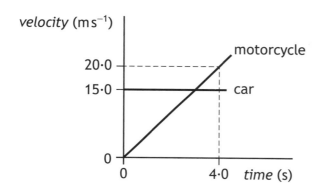

   (a) Calculate the initial acceleration of the motorcycle.

   Space for working and answer

   3

   (b) Determine the distance between the car and motorcycle at $4 \cdot 0 \, \text{s}$.

   Space for working and answer

   4

MARKS | DO NOT WRITE IN THIS MARGIN

1.   (continued)

(c)   The total mass of the motorcycle and rider is 290 kg. At a time of 2·0 s the driving force on the motorcycle is 1800 N.

(i)   Determine the frictional force acting on the motorcycle at this time.

Space for working and answer

4

(ii)   Explain why the driving force must be increased with time to maintain a constant acceleration.

2

MARKS | DO NOT WRITE IN THIS MARGIN

1. (continued)

(d) The driving force on the motorcycle reaches its maximum value at 5·0 s and then remains constant.

The velocity-time graph for the motorcycle during the first 4·0 s is shown below.

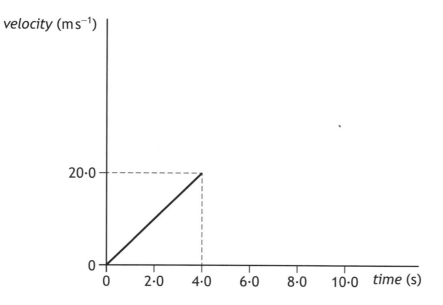

Extend the graph to show how the velocity of the motorcycle varies between 4·0 s and 10·0 s.

Additional numerical values on the velocity axis are **not** required.   1

(An additional graph, if required, can be found on *page forty-two*.)

[Turn over

MARKS | DO NOT WRITE IN THIS MARGIN

2. When a car brakes kinetic energy is turned into heat and sound.

In order to make cars more efficient some manufacturers have developed kinetic energy recovery systems (KERS). These systems store some of the energy that would otherwise be lost as heat and sound.

Estimate the maximum energy that could be stored in such a system when a car brakes.

Cleary show your working for the calculation and any estimates you have made.   4

Space for working and answer

MARKS | DO NOT WRITE IN THIS MARGIN

3.   (a)   A gymnast of mass 42 kg is practising on a trampoline.

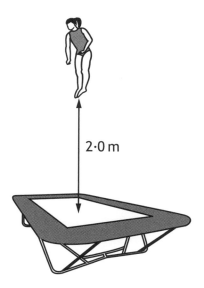

2·0 m

   (i)   At maximum height the gymnast's feet are 2·0 m above the trampoline.

Show that the speed of the gymnast, as they land on the trampoline, is $6\cdot3\,\mathrm{m\,s^{-1}}$.

Space for working and answer

2

   (ii)   The gymnast rebounds with a speed of $5\cdot3\,\mathrm{m\,s^{-1}}$.

Calculate the magnitude of the change in momentum of the gymnast.

Space for working and answer

3

MARKS | DO NOT WRITE IN THIS MARGIN

3. (a) (continued)

(iii) The gymnast was in contact with the trampoline for 0·50 s.

Calculate the magnitude of the average force exerted by the trampoline on the gymnast.

3

Space for working and answer

MARKS | DO NOT WRITE IN THIS MARGIN

3.   (continued)

(b) Another gymnast is practising on a piece of equipment called the rings. The gymnast grips two wooden rings suspended above the gym floor by strong vertical ropes as shown.

The gymnast now stretches out their arms until each rope makes an angle of 10° with the vertical as shown.

Explain why the tension in each rope increases as the gymnast stretches out their arms.

2

[Turn over

MARKS | DO NOT WRITE IN THIS MARGIN

4. Muons are sub-atomic particles produced when cosmic rays enter the atmosphere about 10 km above the surface of the Earth.

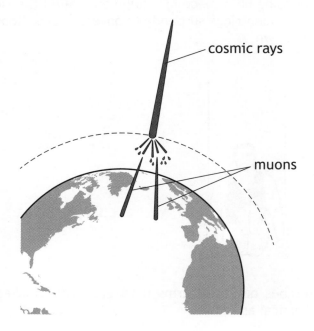

Muons have a mean lifetime of $2 \cdot 2 \times 10^{-6}\,\text{s}$ in their frame of reference. Muons are travelling at $0 \cdot 995c$ relative to an observer on Earth.

(a) Show that the mean distance travelled by the muons in their frame of reference is 660 m.

Space for working and answer

2

(b) Calculate the mean lifetime of the muons measured by an observer on Earth.

Space for working and answer

3

MARKS | DO NOT WRITE IN THIS MARGIN

4.   (continued)

(c) Explain why a greater number of muons are detected on the surface of the Earth than would be expected if relativistic effects were not taken into account.

1

[Turn over

MARKS | DO NOT WRITE IN THIS MARGIN

5. (a) The diagram below represents part of the emission spectrum for the element hydrogen.

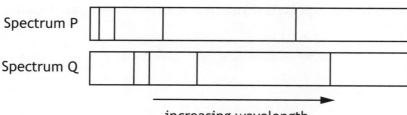

Spectrum P is from a laboratory source.

Spectrum Q shows the equivalent lines from a distant galaxy as observed on the Earth.

(i) Explain why the lines on spectrum Q are in a different position to those on spectrum P.

2

(ii) One of the lines in spectrum P has a wavelength of 656 nm. The equivalent line in spectrum Q is measured to have a wavelength of 676 nm.

Determine the recessional velocity of the galaxy.

5

Space for working and answer

MARKS | DO NOT WRITE IN THIS MARGIN

5. **(continued)**

(b) The recessional velocity of another distant galaxy is $1 \cdot 2 \times 10^7\,\mathrm{m\,s^{-1}}$.

Calculate the approximate distance to this galaxy.   **3**

Space for working and answer

(c) A student explains the expansion of the Universe using an 'expanding balloon model'.

The student draws 'galaxies' on a balloon and then inflates it.

Using your knowledge of physics, comment on this model.   **3**

MARKS | DO NOT WRITE IN THIS MARGIN

6. A linear accelerator is used to accelerate protons.

The accelerator consists of hollow metal tubes placed in a vacuum.

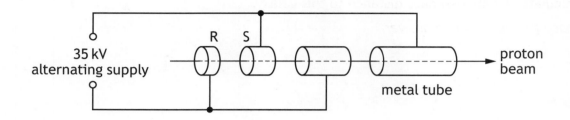

The diagram shows the path of the protons through the accelerator.

Protons are accelerated across the gaps between the tubes by a potential difference of 35 kV.

(a) The protons are travelling at $1{\cdot}2 \times 10^6\,\mathrm{m\,s^{-1}}$ at point R.

    (i) Show that the work done on a proton as it accelerates from R to S is $5{\cdot}6 \times 10^{-15}\,\mathrm{J}$.

       Space for working and answer   **2**

    (ii) Determine the speed of the proton as it reaches S.   **5**

       Space for working and answer

MARKS | DO NOT WRITE IN THIS MARGIN

6. (continued)

(b) (i) Explain why an alternating supply is used in the linear accelerator.

1

(ii) Suggest one reason why the lengths of the tubes increase along the accelerator.

1

(c) In the Large Hadron Collider (LHC) beams of hadrons travel in opposite directions inside a circular accelerator and then collide. The accelerating particles are guided along the collider using strong magnetic fields.

The diagram shows a proton entering a magnetic field.

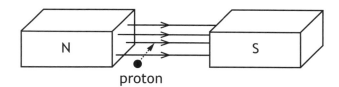

proton

In which direction is this proton initially deflected?

1

[Turn over

MARKS | DO NOT WRITE IN THIS MARGIN

7. The following diagram gives information about the Standard Model of fundamental particles and interactions.

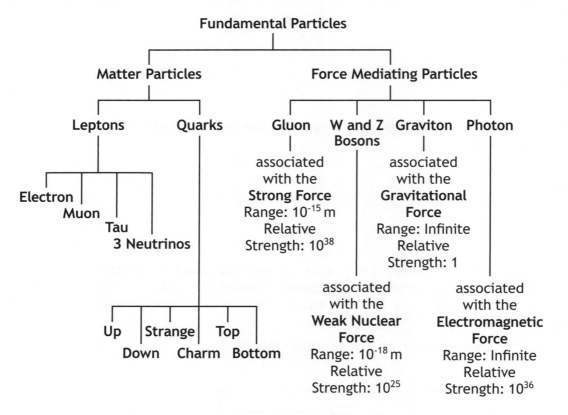

Use information from the diagram and your knowledge of the Standard Model to answer the following questions.

(a) Explain why particles such as leptons and quarks are known as *fundamental particles*.   1

(b) A particle called the sigma plus (Σ^+) has a charge of $+1e$. It contains two different types of quark. It has two up quarks each having a charge of $+\frac{2}{3}e$ and one strange quark.

Determine the charge on the strange quark.   1

MARKS | DO NOT WRITE IN THIS MARGIN

7. (continued)

(c) Explain why the gluon cannot be the force mediating particle for the gravitational force.

2

(d) Compare the relative strength of the strong force with the weak nuclear force in terms of orders of magnitude.

1

(e) A neutron decays into a proton, an electron and an antineutrino.

The equation for this decay is

$$_0^1n \rightarrow \, _1^1p + \, _{-1}^0e + \bar{\nu}_e$$

State the name of this type of decay.

1

[Turn over

MARKS | DO NOT WRITE IN THIS MARGIN

8. The following statement represents a fusion reaction.

$$4\,^{1}_{1}H \rightarrow \,^{4}_{2}He + 2\,^{0}_{1}e^{+}$$

The masses of the particles involved in the reaction are shown in the table.

Particle	Mass (kg)
$^{1}_{1}H$	$1 \cdot 673 \times 10^{-27}$
$^{4}_{2}He$	$6 \cdot 646 \times 10^{-27}$
$^{0}_{1}e^{+}$	negligible

(a) Calculate the energy released in this reaction.   4

Space for working and answer

MARKS | DO NOT WRITE IN THIS MARGIN

8. (continued)

(b) Calculate the energy released when 0·20 kg of hydrogen is converted to helium by this reaction.

3

Space for working and answer

(c) Fusion reactors are being developed that use this type of reaction as an energy source.

Explain why this type of fusion reaction is hard to sustain in these reactors.

1

[Turn over

MARKS | DO NOT WRITE IN THIS MARGIN

9. A student carries out an experiment to investigate how irradiance on a surface varies with distance from a small lamp.

Irradiance is measured using a light meter.

The distance between the small lamp and the light meter is measured with a metre stick.

The apparatus is set up in a darkened laboratory as shown.

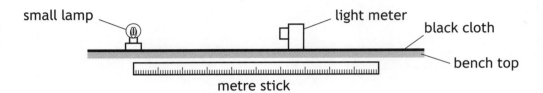

The following results are obtained.

Distance from source (m)	0·200	0·300	0·400	0·500
Irradiance (units)	672	302	170	110

(a) State what is meant by the term *irradiance*.   1

(b) Use **all** the data to find the relationship between irradiance I and distance d from the source.

You may wish to use the square-ruled paper on *page thirty-seven*.   3

Space for working and answer

MAR

9. **(continued)**

(c) Suggest the purpose of the black cloth placed on top of the bench in the experimental set-up.   1

(d) The small lamp is replaced by a laser.

Light from the laser is shone onto the light meter.

A reading is taken from the light meter when the distance between the light meter and the laser is 0·200 m.

The distance is now increased to 0·500 m.

The reading on the light meter does not change.

Suggest why the reading on the light meter does not change.   1

[Turn over

MARKS | DO NOT WRITE IN THIS MARGIN

...mits electrons when certain wavelengths of electromagnetic ...cident on it.

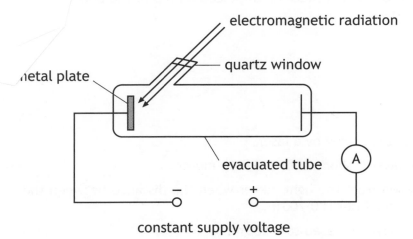

constant supply voltage

The work function of the metal is $2 \cdot 24 \times 10^{-19}$ J.

(a) Electrons are released when electromagnetic radiation of wavelength 525 nm is incident on the surface of the metal plate.

   (i) Show that the energy of each photon of the incident radiation is $3 \cdot 79 \times 10^{-19}$ J.

   Space for working and answer

4

   (ii) Determine the maximum kinetic energy of an electron released from the surface of the metal plate.

   Space for working and answer

1

MARKS | DO NOT WRITE IN THIS MARGIN

10. (continued)

(b) The frequency of the incident radiation in now varied through a range of values.

The maximum kinetic energy of electrons leaving the metal plate is determined for each frequency.

A graph of this maximum kinetic energy against frequency is shown.

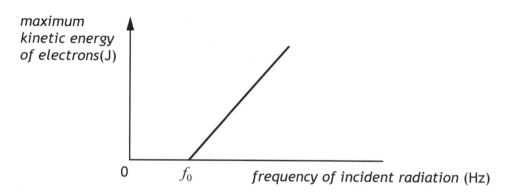

(i) Explain why no electrons leave the metal plate when the frequency of the incident radiation is below f_0.   **1**

(ii) Calculate the frequency f_0.   **3**

Space for working and answer

MARKS | DO NOT WRITE IN THIS MARGIN

10. **(continued)**

(c) The use of analogies from everyday life can help better understanding of physics concepts. Throwing different balls at a coconut shy to dislodge a coconut is an analogy which can help understanding of the photoelectric effect .

Use your knowledge of physics to comment on this analogy.   **3**

MARKS | DO NOT WRITE IN THIS MARGIN

11. A helium-neon laser produces a beam of monochromatic light.

A student directs this laser beam onto a double slit arrangement as shown in the diagram.

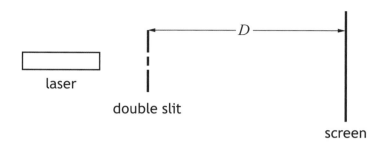

A pattern of bright red fringes is observed on the screen.

(a) Explain, in terms of waves, why bright red fringes are produced. **1**

[Turn over

MARKS | DO NOT WRITE IN THIS MARGIN

11.   **(continued)**

(b) The average separation Δx between adjacent fringes is given by the relationship

$$\Delta x = \frac{\lambda D}{d}$$

where: λ is the wavelength of the light
D is the distance between the double slit and the screen
d is the distance between the two slits

The diagram shows the value measured by the student of the distance between a series of fringes and the uncertainty in this measurement.

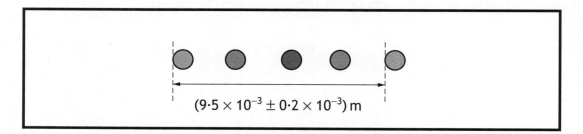

$(9{\cdot}5 \times 10^{-3} \pm 0{\cdot}2 \times 10^{-3})\,\text{m}$

The student measures the distance D between the double slit and the screen as $(0{\cdot}750 \pm 0{\cdot}001)$ m.

(i) Calculate the best estimate of the distance between the two slits.

An uncertainty in the calculated value is not required.   **3**

Space for working and answer

MARKS | DO NOT WRITE IN THIS MARGIN

11. (b) (continued)

(ii) The student wishes to determine more precisely the value of the distance between the two slits d.

Show, by calculation, which of the student's measurements should be taken more precisely in order to achieve this.

You must indicate clearly which measurement you have identified.   **3**

Space for working and answer

(c) The helium-neon laser is replaced by a laser emitting green light. No other changes are made to the experimental set-up.

Explain the effect this change has on the separation of the fringes observed on the screen.   **2**

[Turn over

MARKS | DO NOT WRITE IN THIS MARGIN

12. A technician investigates the path of laser light as it passes through a glass tank filled with water. The light enters the glass tank along the normal at **C** then reflects off a mirror submerged in the water.

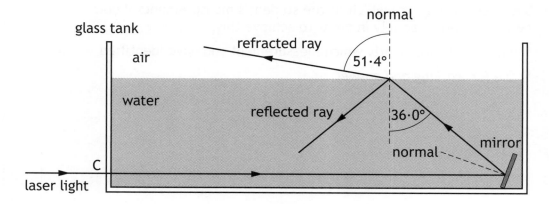

not to scale

(a) Show that the refractive index of water for this laser light is 1·33.

Space for working and answer

2

(b) The mirror is now adjusted until the light strikes the surface of the water at the critical angle.

   (i) State what is meant by the *critical angle*.

1

   (ii) Calculate the critical angle for this light in the water.

Space for working and answer

3

MARKS | DO NOT WRITE IN THIS MARGIN

13. The following circuit is used to determine the internal resistance r of a battery of EMF E.

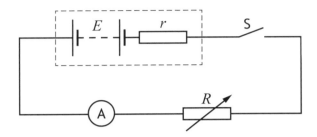

The variable resistor provides known values of resistance R.

For each value of resistance R the switch S is closed and the current I is noted.

For each current, the value of $\frac{1}{I}$ is calculated.

In one such experiment, the following graph of R against $\frac{1}{I}$ is obtained.

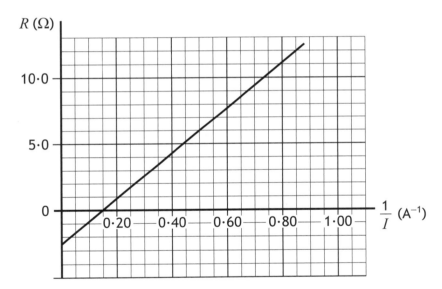

Conservation of energy applied to the complete circuit gives the following relationship.

$$R = \frac{E}{I} - r$$

This relationship is in the form of the equation of a straight line

$$y = mx + c$$

where m is the gradient and c is the y-intercept.

MARKS | DO NOT WRITE IN THIS MARGIN

13.   **(continued)**

(a)   Use information from the graph to determine:

(i)   the internal resistance of the battery   1

(ii)   the EMF of the battery.   2
Space for working and answer

(b)   The battery is accidentally short-circuited.
Calculate the current in the battery when this happens.   3
Space for working and answer

MARKS | DO NOT WRITE IN THIS MARGIN

14. A 220 μF capacitor is charged using the circuit shown.

The 12 V battery has negligible internal resistance.

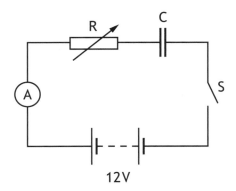

The capacitor is initially uncharged.

The switch S is closed. The charging current is kept constant at $3 \cdot 0 \times 10^{-5}$ A by adjusting the resistance of variable resistor R.

(a) Calculate the resistance of the variable resistor R just after the switch is closed.   **3**

Space for working and answer

(b) (i) Calculate the charge on the capacitor 25 s after switch S is closed.   **3**

Space for working and answer

MARKS | DO NOT WRITE IN THIS MARGIN

14. **(b)** **(continued)**

(ii) Calculate the potential difference across R at this time.   4

Space for working and answer

MARKS | DO NOT WRITE IN THIS MARGIN

15. The electrical conductivity of solids can be explained using band theory.

The diagrams below show the distributions of the valence and conduction bands of materials classified as conductors, insulators and semiconductors.

Shaded areas represent bands occupied by electrons.

The band gap is also indicated.

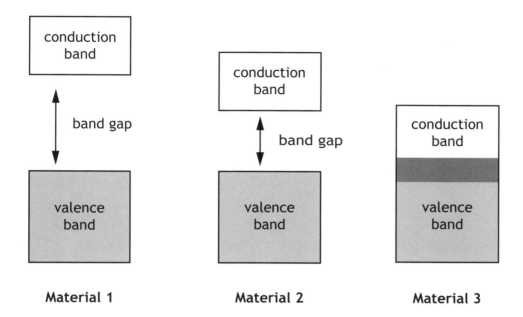

Material 1   Material 2   Material 3

(a) State which material is a semiconductor.   1

[Turn over

15. **(continued)**

(b) An LED is made from semiconductor material that has been doped with impurities to create a p-n junction.

The diagram represents the band structure of an LED.

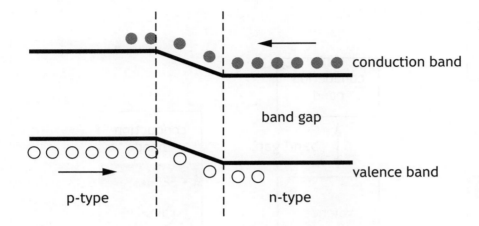

A voltage is applied across an LED so that it is forward biased and emits light.

Using **band theory**, explain how the LED emits light.

3

MARKS | DO NOT WRITE IN THIS MARGIN

16. A group of students carries out an experiment to investigate the transmission of light through an optical fibre.

Red light is transmitted through a loop of optical fibre and detected by a photodiode connected to a voltmeter as shown.

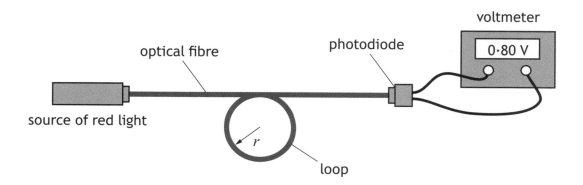

The photodiode produces a voltage proportional to the irradiance of light incident on it.

The students vary the radius, r, of the loop of the optical fibre and measure the voltage produced by the photodiode.

The results are shown in the table.

Radius of loop (mm)	Voltage (V)
5	0·48
10	0·68
15	0·76
20	0·79
30	0·80
40	0·80

(a) Using the square-ruled paper provided on *page thirty-eight*, draw a graph of these results.

3

[Turn over

MARKS | DO NOT WRITE IN THIS MARGIN

16.   (continued)

(b) For use in communication systems, the amount of light transmitted through a loop of optical fibre must be at least 75% of the value of the fibre with no loop.

With no loop in this fibre the reading on the voltmeter is 0·80 V.

Use your graph to estimate the minimum radius of loop when using this fibre in communication systems.

1

(c) Using the same apparatus, the students now wish to determine a better estimate of the true value of minimum radius of loop when using this fibre in communication systems.

Suggest **two** improvements to the experimental procedure that would achieve this.

2

[END OF SPECIMEN QUESTION PAPER]

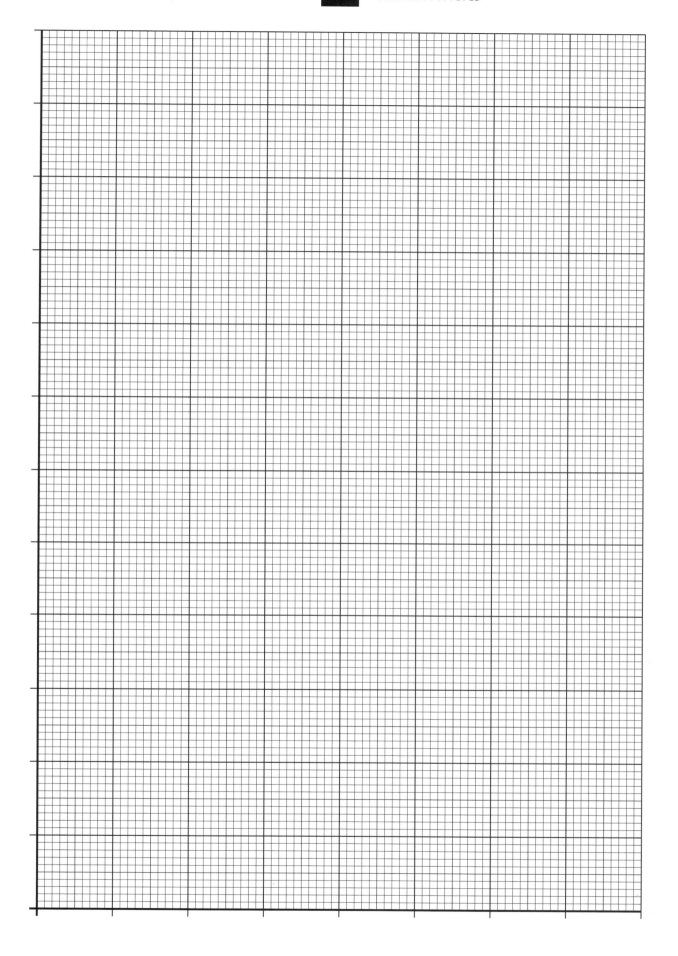

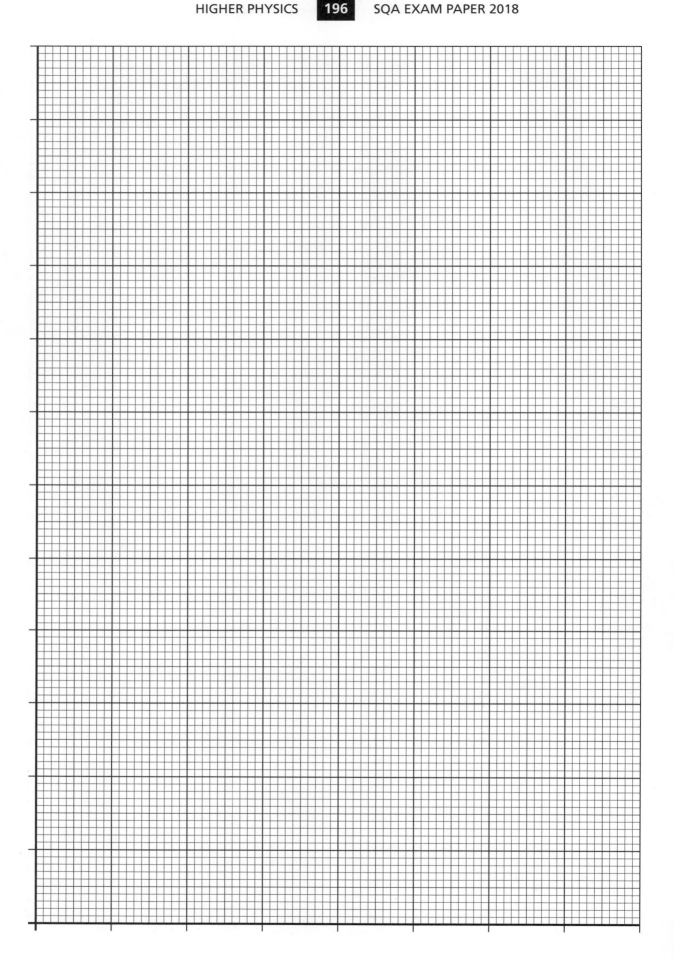

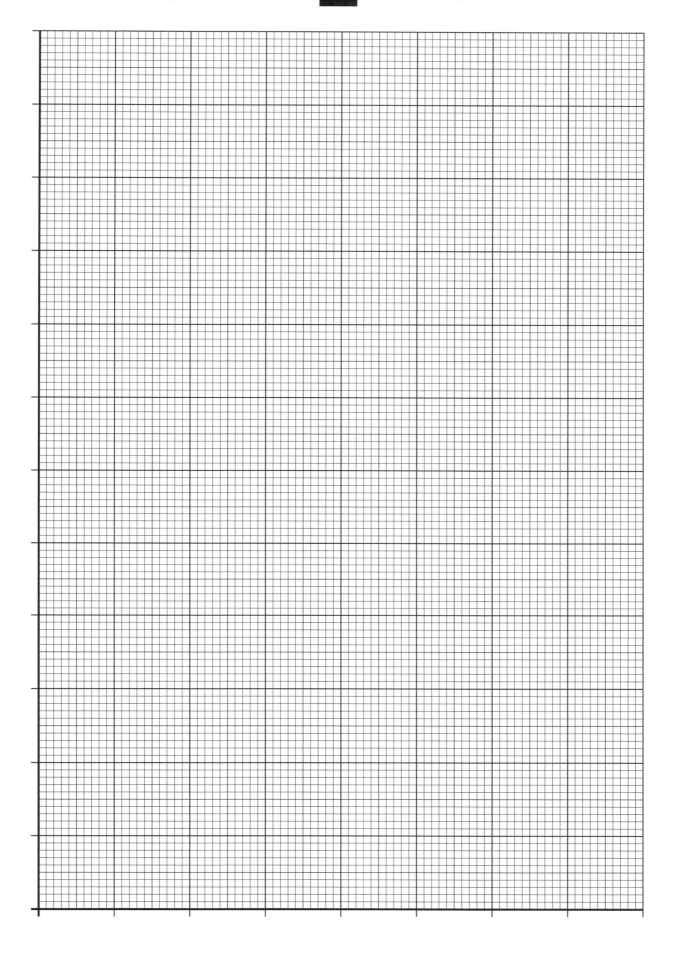

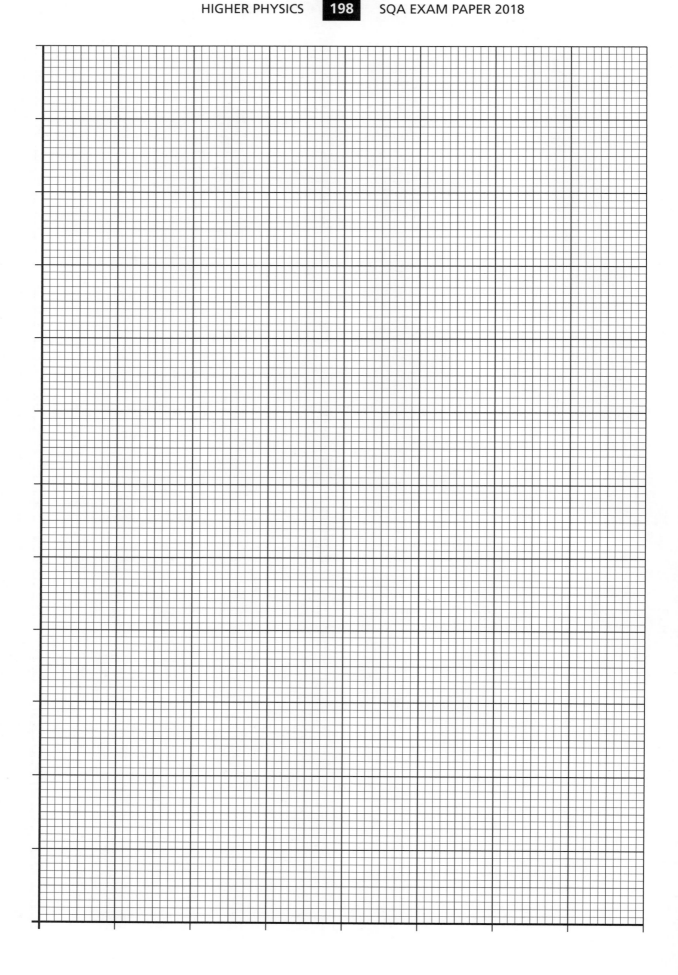

MARKS | DO NOT WRITE IN THIS MARGIN

ADDITIONAL SPACE FOR ANSWERS AND ROUGH WORK

Additional graph for use with Question 1 (d)

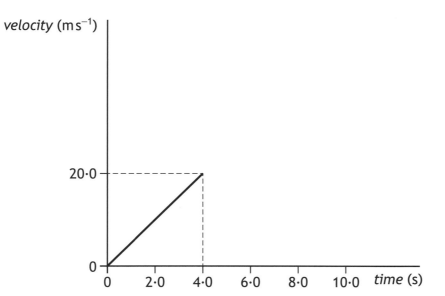

ADDITIONAL SPACE FOR ANSWERS AND ROUGH WORK

MARKS | DO NOT WRITE IN THIS MARGIN

National
Qualifications
SPECIMEN ONLY

S857/76/11

Physics
Paper 2 — Relationships sheet

Date — Not applicable

Relationships required for Physics Higher

$d = \bar{v}t$

$s = \bar{v}t$

$v = u + at$

$s = ut + \frac{1}{2}at^2$

$v^2 = u^2 + 2as$

$s = \frac{1}{2}(u + v)t$

$F = ma$

$W = mg$

$E_w = Fd, \text{ or } W = Fd$

$E_p = mgh$

$E_k = \frac{1}{2}mv^2$

$P = \dfrac{E}{t}$

$p = mv$

$Ft = mv - mu$

$F = G\dfrac{m_1 m_2}{r^2}$

$t' = \dfrac{t}{\sqrt{1 - \left(\dfrac{v}{c}\right)^2}}$

$l' = l\sqrt{1 - \left(\dfrac{v}{c}\right)^2}$

$f_o = f_s\left(\dfrac{v}{v \pm v_s}\right)$

$z = \dfrac{\lambda_{observed} - \lambda_{rest}}{\lambda_{rest}}$

$z = \dfrac{v}{c}$

$v = H_0 d$

$W = QV$

$E = mc^2$

$I = \dfrac{P}{A}$

$I = \dfrac{k}{d^2}$

$I_1 d_1^2 = I_2 d_2^2$

$E = hf$

$E_k = hf - hf_0$

$v = f\lambda$

$E_2 - E_1 = hf$

$d\sin\theta = m\lambda$

$n = \dfrac{\sin\theta_1}{\sin\theta_2}$

$\dfrac{\sin\theta_1}{\sin\theta_2} = \dfrac{\lambda_1}{\lambda_2} = \dfrac{v_1}{v_2}$

$\sin\theta_c = \dfrac{1}{n}$

$V_{rms} = \dfrac{V_{peak}}{\sqrt{2}}$

$I_{rms} = \dfrac{I_{peak}}{\sqrt{2}}$

$T = \dfrac{1}{f}$

$V = IR$

$P = IV = I^2 R = \dfrac{V^2}{R}$

$R_T = R_1 + R_2 + \ldots$

$\dfrac{1}{R_T} = \dfrac{1}{R_1} + \dfrac{1}{R_2} + \ldots$

$V_1 = \left(\dfrac{R_1}{R_1 + R_2}\right)V_s$

$\dfrac{V_1}{V_2} = \dfrac{R_1}{R_2}$

$E = V + Ir$

$C = \dfrac{Q}{V}$

$Q = It$

$E = \frac{1}{2}QV = \frac{1}{2}CV^2 = \frac{1}{2}\dfrac{Q^2}{C}$

path difference $= m\lambda$ or $\left(m + \frac{1}{2}\right)\lambda$ where $m = 0, 1, 2\ldots$

random uncertainty $= \dfrac{\text{max. value} - \text{min. value}}{\text{number of values}}$

or

$\Delta R = \dfrac{R_{max} - R_{min}}{n}$

Additional relationships

Circle

circumference $= 2\pi r$

area $= \pi r^2$

Sphere

area $= 4\pi r^2$

volume $= \frac{4}{3}\pi r^3$

Trigonometry

$\sin\theta = \dfrac{\text{opposite}}{\text{hypotenuse}}$

$\cos\theta = \dfrac{\text{adjacent}}{\text{hypotenuse}}$

$\tan\theta = \dfrac{\text{opposite}}{\text{adjacent}}$

$\sin^2\theta + \cos^2\theta = 1$

Key

| Atomic number |
| Symbol |
| Electron arrangement |
| Name |

Transition elements

Group 1	Group 2												Group 3	Group 4	Group 5	Group 6	Group 7	Group 0
(1)	(2)	(3)	(4)	(5)	(6)	(7)	(8)	(9)	(10)	(11)	(12)		(13)	(14)	(15)	(16)	(17)	(18)

1 **H** 1 Hydrogen																		2 **He** 2 Helium
3 **Li** 2,1 Lithium	4 **Be** 2,2 Beryllium												5 **B** 2,3 Boron	6 **C** 2,4 Carbon	7 **N** 2,5 Nitrogen	8 **O** 2,6 Oxygen	9 **F** 2,7 Fluorine	10 **Ne** 2,8 Neon
11 **Na** 2,8,1 Sodium	12 **Mg** 2,8,2 Magnesium												13 **Al** 2,8,3 Aluminium	14 **Si** 2,8,4 Silicon	15 **P** 2,8,5 Phosphorus	16 **S** 2,8,6 Sulfur	17 **Cl** 2,8,7 Chlorine	18 **Ar** 2,8,8 Argon
19 **K** 2,8,8,1 Potassium	20 **Ca** 2,8,8,2 Calcium	21 **Sc** 2,8,9,2 Scandium	22 **Ti** 2,8,10,2 Titanium	23 **V** 2,8,11,2 Vanadium	24 **Cr** 2,8,13,1 Chromium	25 **Mn** 2,8,13,2 Manganese	26 **Fe** 2,8,14,2 Iron	27 **Co** 2,8,15,2 Cobalt	28 **Ni** 2,8,16,2 Nickel	29 **Cu** 2,8,18,1 Copper	30 **Zn** 2,8,18,2 Zinc		31 **Ga** 2,8,18,3 Gallium	32 **Ge** 2,8,18,4 Germanium	33 **As** 2,8,18,5 Arsenic	34 **Se** 2,8,18,6 Selenium	35 **Br** 2,8,18,7 Bromine	36 **Kr** 2,8,18,8 Krypton
37 **Rb** 2,8,18,8,1 Rubidium	38 **Sr** 2,8,18,8,2 Strontium	39 **Y** 2,8,18,9,2 Yttrium	40 **Zr** 2,8,18,10,2 Zirconium	41 **Nb** 2,8,18,12,1 Niobium	42 **Mo** 2,8,18,13,1 Molybdenum	43 **Tc** 2,8,18,13,2 Technetium	44 **Ru** 2,8,18,15,1 Ruthenium	45 **Rh** 2,8,18,16,1 Rhodium	46 **Pd** 2,8,18,18,0 Palladium	47 **Ag** 2,8,18,18,1 Silver	48 **Cd** 2,8,18,18,2 Cadmium		49 **In** 2,8,18,18,3 Indium	50 **Sn** 2,8,18,18,4 Tin	51 **Sb** 2,8,18,18,5 Antimony	52 **Te** 2,8,18,18,6 Tellurium	53 **I** 2,8,18,18,7 Iodine	54 **Xe** 2,8,18,18,8 Xenon
55 **Cs** 2,8,18,18,8,1 Caesium	56 **Ba** 2,8,18,18,8,2 Barium	57 **La** 2,8,18,18,9,2 Lanthanum	72 **Hf** 2,8,18,32,10,2 Hafnium	73 **Ta** 2,8,18,32,11,2 Tantalum	74 **W** 2,8,18,32,12,2 Tungsten	75 **Re** 2,8,18,32,13,2 Rhenium	76 **Os** 2,8,18,32,14,2 Osmium	77 **Ir** 2,8,18,32,15,2 Iridium	78 **Pt** 2,8,18,32,17,1 Platinum	79 **Au** 2,8,18,32,18,1 Gold	80 **Hg** 2,8,18,32,18,2 Mercury		81 **Tl** 2,8,18,32,18,3 Thallium	82 **Pb** 2,8,18,32,18,4 Lead	83 **Bi** 2,8,18,32,18,5 Bismuth	84 **Po** 2,8,18,32,18,6 Polonium	85 **At** 2,8,18,32,18,7 Astatine	86 **Rn** 2,8,18,32,18,8 Radon
87 **Fr** 2,8,18,32,18,8,1 Francium	88 **Ra** 2,8,18,32,18,8,2 Radium	89 **Ac** 2,8,18,32,18,9,2 Actinium	104 **Rf** 2,8,18,32,32,10,2 Rutherfordium	105 **Db** 2,8,18,32,32,11,2 Dubnium	106 **Sg** 2,8,18,32,32,12,2 Seaborgium	107 **Bh** 2,8,18,32,32,13,2 Bohrium	108 **Hs** 2,8,18,32,32,14,2 Hassium	109 **Mt** 2,8,18,32,32,15,2 Meitnerium	110 **Ds** 2,8,18,32,32,17,1 Darmstadtium	111 **Rg** 2,8,18,32,32,18,1 Roentgenium	112 **Cn** 2,8,18,32,32,18,2 Copernicium							

Lanthanides

57 **La** 2,8,18,18,9,2 Lanthanum	58 **Ce** 2,8,18,20,8,2 Cerium	59 **Pr** 2,8,18,21,8,2 Praseodymium	60 **Nd** 2,8,18,22,8,2 Neodymium	61 **Pm** 2,8,18,23,8,2 Promethium	62 **Sm** 2,8,18,24,8,2 Samarium	63 **Eu** 2,8,18,25,8,2 Europium	64 **Gd** 2,8,18,25,9,2 Gadolinium	65 **Tb** 2,8,18,27,8,2 Terbium	66 **Dy** 2,8,18,28,8,2 Dysprosium	67 **Ho** 2,8,18,29,8,2 Holmium	68 **Er** 2,8,18,30,8,2 Erbium	69 **Tm** 2,8,18,31,8,2 Thulium	70 **Yb** 2,8,18,32,8,2 Ytterbium	71 **Lu** 2,8,18,32,9,2 Lutetium

Actinides

89 **Ac** 2,8,18,32,18,9,2 Actinium	90 **Th** 2,8,18,32,18,10,2 Thorium	91 **Pa** 2,8,18,32,20,9,2 Protactinium	92 **U** 2,8,18,32,21,9,2 Uranium	93 **Np** 2,8,18,32,22,9,2 Neptunium	94 **Pu** 2,8,18,32,24,8,2 Plutonium	95 **Am** 2,8,18,32,25,8,2 Americium	96 **Cm** 2,8,18,32,25,9,2 Curium	97 **Bk** 2,8,18,32,27,8,2 Berkelium	98 **Cf** 2,8,18,32,28,8,2 Californium	99 **Es** 2,8,18,32,29,8,2 Einsteinium	100 **Fm** 2,8,18,32,30,8,2 Fermium	101 **Md** 2,8,18,32,31,8,2 Mendelevium	102 **No** 2,8,18,32,32,8,2 Nobelium	103 **Lr** 2,8,18,32,32,9,2 Lawrencium

HIGHER
Answers

SECTION 1

Question	Answer	Mark
1.	A	1
2.	B	1
3.	C	1
4.	B	1
5.	B	1
6.	C	1
7.	D	1
8.	A	1
9.	D	1
10.	B	1
11.	E	1
12.	E	1
13.	D	1
14.	D	1
15.	A	1
16.	A	1
17.	B	1
18.	E	1
19.	E	1
20.	A	1

SECTION 2

Question			Answer	Max mark
1.	(a)	(i)	The velocity increases by $0 \cdot 32$ m s^{-1} each/per second	1
		(ii)	$s = ut + \frac{1}{2}at^2$ (1) $s = \left((0 \times 25)\right) + \left(0 \cdot 5 \times 0 \cdot 32 \times 25^2\right)$ (1) $s = 100$ m (1)	3
	(b)	(i)	$f_o = f_s\left(\dfrac{v}{v \pm v_s}\right)$ (1) $290 = 270\left(\dfrac{340}{340 - v_s}\right)$ (1) $v_s = 23\,\text{ms}^{-1}$ (1)	3
		(ii)	Statement that there are fewer wavefronts per second OR The wavefronts are further apart OR The wavelength increases OR Diagram showing wavefronts closer together ahead of the train and further apart behind it OR any similar response	1

Question			Answer	Max mark
2.	(a)	(i)	(Total momentum before = total momentum after) $m_x u_x + m_y u_y = m_x v_x + m_y v_y$ (1) $(0 \cdot 180 \times 2 \cdot 60) + (0 \cdot 180 \times -1 \cdot 80)$ $= (0 \cdot 180 v_x + 0 \cdot 180 \times 2 \cdot 38)$ (1) $0 \cdot 468 - 0 \cdot 324 = 0 \cdot 180 v_x + 0 \cdot 4284$ $v_x = -1 \cdot 58$ m s^{-1} (1) (Accept "1·58 ms^{-1} to the left" or an indication of direction, eg arrow left)	3
		(ii)	<u>Kinetic</u> energy is lost/greater before the collision than after	1
	(b)	(i)	$Ft = mv - mu$ (1) $F \times 0 \cdot 040$ $= \left(0 \cdot 180 \times 0 \cdot 84\right)$ $- \left(0 \cdot 180 \times 0\right)$ (1) $F = 3 \cdot 8\text{N}$ (1)	3
		(ii)	$\left(\dfrac{0 \cdot 01}{0 \cdot 84} \times 100 = 1 \cdot 2\right)$ $\left(\dfrac{0 \cdot 001}{0 \cdot 180} \times 100 = 0 \cdot 56\right)$ $\dfrac{0 \cdot 001}{0 \cdot 040} \times 100 \ (= 2 \cdot 5)$ (1) (Uncertainty in F is) 2·5% (1)	2
3.	(a)	(i)	$v = u + at$ (1) $0 = 5 \cdot 6 + (-9 \cdot 8)t$ (1) $t = 0 \cdot 57$ s (1)	3
		(ii)	$v^2 = u^2 + 2as$ (1) $\left(-7 \cdot 7\right)^2 = 0^2 + 2 \times (-9 \cdot 8)s$ (1) $s = -3 \cdot 0\,\text{m}$ (1) (Distance = 3·0 m)	3
	(b)		Starting point greater than 5·6 (1) Final point beyond −7·7 (1) Acceptably parallel line (1)	3

4.			Demonstrates no understanding
			          0 marks
			 Demonstrates limited understanding 1 mark
			 Demonstrates reasonable understanding 2 marks
			 Demonstrates good understanding
			          3 marks
			 This is an open-ended question.
			
			 1 mark: The student has demonstrated a limited understanding of the physics involved. The student has made some statement(s) which is/are relevant to the situation, showing that at least a little of the physics within the problem is understood.
				3

Question			Answer	Max mark
			2 marks: The student has demonstrated a reasonable understanding of the physics involved. The student makes some statement(s) which is/are relevant to the situation, showing that the problem is understood.	
			3 marks: The maximum available mark would be awarded to a student who has demonstrated a good understanding of the physics involved. The student shows a good comprehension of the physics of the situation and has provided a logically correct answer to the question posed. This type of response might include a statement of the principles involved, a relationship or an equation, and the application of these to respond to the problem. This does not mean the answer has to be what might be termed an "excellent" answer or a "complete" one.	
5.	(a)	(i)	$\left(\dfrac{3 \cdot 83 \times 10^{30}}{5 \cdot 69 \times 10^{27}}\right) = 673$ (1) (Star is) 3 (orders of magnitude) <u>greater</u> (1) **OR** <u>Exoplanet</u> is 3 (orders of magnitude) <u>smaller</u>	2
		(ii)	$F = G\dfrac{m_1 m_2}{r^2}$ (1) $F = 6 \cdot 67 \times 10^{-11}\dfrac{5 \cdot 69 \times 10^{27} \times 3 \cdot 83 \times 10^{30}}{\left(3 \cdot 14 \times 10^{11}\right)^2}$ (1) $F = 1 \cdot 47 \times 10^{25}\,\text{N}$ (1)	3
	(b)	(i)	$z = \dfrac{v}{c}$ (1) $z = \dfrac{6 \cdot 60 \times 10^3}{3 \cdot 00 \times 10^8}$ (1) $z = 2 \cdot 20 \times 10^{-5}$ (1)	3
		(ii)	Greater (than)	1
6.	(a)		E_0 to E_3 $E_0 \rightarrow E_3$ Between E_0 and E_3	1
	(b)		$E_2 - E_1 = hf$ (1) $-1 \cdot 36 \times 10^{-19} - \left(-5 \cdot 42 \times 10^{-19}\right)$ $= 6 \cdot 63 \times 10^{-34} \times f$ (1) $f = 6 \cdot 12 \times 10^{14}\,\text{Hz}$ (1)	3
7.	(a)		They are composed of other particles/quarks, (fundamental particles are not)	1
	(b)	(i)	Baryons are (hadrons as they are) composed of (three) <u>quarks</u> (1) Mesons/some hadrons are made from a quark − anti-quark pair so are not baryons (1)	2

Question			Answer	Max mark
		(ii)	$-1/3(e)$	1
	(c)	(i)	Strong (nuclear force)	1
		(ii)	Gluon	1
	(d)		$t' = \dfrac{t}{\sqrt{1-\left(\dfrac{v}{c}\right)^2}}$ (1) $t' = \dfrac{1 \cdot 5 \times 10^{-10}}{\sqrt{1-\dfrac{\left(0 \cdot 9c\right)^2}{c^2}}}$ (1) $t' = 3 \cdot 4 \times 10^{-10}\,\text{s}$ (1)	3
8.	(a)	(i)	W or $E_W = QV$ (1) $= 1 \cdot 60 \times 10^{-19} \times 2 \cdot 50 \times 10^3$ (1) $= 4 \cdot 00 \times 10^{-16}\,\text{J}$ (1)	3
		(ii)	Particle (always) accelerates in the same direction/forwards **OR** Force on particle/electron is always in same direction **OR** Ensure the direction of the electric field is correct when particle/electron passes between (alternate) gaps	1
	(b)	(i)	Out of page	1
		(ii)	(Magnetic fields are in) <u>opposite</u> directions (1) (Magnetic field in) S is <u>stronger</u> than (field in) R (1)	2
	(c)		$E_K = \dfrac{1}{2}mv^2$ (1) $4 \cdot 16 \times 10^{-17} = \dfrac{1}{2} \times 9 \cdot 11 \times 10^{-31} \times v^2$ (1) $v = 9 \cdot 56 \times 10^6\,\text{ms}^{-1}$ (1)	3
9.	(a)		(Two) small nuclei combine to form a larger nucleus	1
	(b)	(i)	(Some) mass (is lost and) <u>converted</u> to energy	1
		(ii)	Mass before: $5 \cdot 008 \times 10^{-27} + 3 \cdot 344 \times 10^{-27}$ $\qquad\qquad = 8 \cdot 352 \times 10^{-27}$ Mass after: $6 \cdot 646 \times 10^{-27} + 1 \cdot 673 \times 10^{-27}$ $\qquad\qquad = 8 \cdot 319 \times 10^{-27}$ Mass "lost": $0 \cdot 033 \times 10^{-27}$ (kg) (1) $E = mc^2$ (1) $E = 0 \cdot 033 \times 10^{-27} \times (3 \cdot 00 \times 10^8)^2$ (1) $E = 2 \cdot 97 \times 10^{-12}\,\text{J}$ (1)	4
10.	(a)		Waves <u>meet</u> in phase OR Crest <u>meets</u> crest OR Trough <u>meets</u> trough OR Path difference $= m\lambda$	1
	(b)	(i)	Statement that λ = gradient (1) OR link λ to the gradient Subs to calculate gradient (1) $\lambda = 4 \cdot 8 \times 10^{-7}\,\text{m}$ (1)	3

Question			Answer		Max mark
		(ii)	$(d = 2 \times 10^{-6}$ gives:$)$ $\frac{1}{d} = 0.50 \times 10^6$ (1) $sin\theta = 0.24$ from graph (1) $\theta = 14°$ (1)		3
	(c)		Any two correct answers from: Repeat measurements Use additional gratings Move screen further away Use second order maxima to determine θ Measure angle from first order to first order		2
11.			Demonstrates no understanding 0 marks Demonstrates limited understanding 1 mark Demonstrates reasonable understanding 2 marks Demonstrates good understanding 3 marks This is an open-ended question. **1 mark:** The student has demonstrated a limited understanding of the physics involved. The student has made some statement(s) which is/are relevant to the situation, showing that at least a little of the physics within the problem is understood. **2 marks:** The student has demonstrated a reasonable understanding of the physics involved. The student makes some statement(s) which is/are relevant to the situation, showing that the problem is understood. **3 marks:** The maximum available mark would be awarded to a student who has demonstrated a good understanding of the physics involved. The student shows a good comprehension of the physics of the situation and has provided a logically correct answer to the question posed. This type of response might include a statement of the principles involved, a relationship or an equation, and the application of these to respond to the problem. This does not mean the answer has to be what might be termed an "excellent" answer or a "complete" one.		3
12.	(a)		1·5 J (of energy) is <u>supplied to/ gained by</u> each coulomb (of charge passing through the cell)		1

Question			Answer		Max mark
	(b)	(i)	Lost volts $= Ir$ (1) Lost volts $= 64 \times 10^{-3} \times (2 \times 2.7)$ (1) Lost volts $= 0.35$ V		2
		(ii)	$V = 2.7$ V		1
		(iii)	$P = IV$ (1) $P = 64 \times 10^{-3} \times 2.7$ (1) $P = 0.17$ W (1)		3
	(c)		$V = E - Ir$ $V = 6.0 - (26 \times 10^{-3} \times (4 \times 2.7))$ (1) $V = 5.7192$ (V) $R = \frac{V_R}{I}$ (both formulae) (1) $R = \frac{5.7192 - 3.6}{26 \times 10^{-3}}$ (1) $R = 82$ Ω (1)		4
13.	(a)		$V = IR$ (1) $12 = I \times 6800$ (1) $I = 1.8 \times 10^{-3}$ A (1)		3
	(b)		The (circuit/total) resistance is less (1) <u>Initial</u> charging current is greater (1)		2
14.	(a)		Photovoltaic (effect)		1
	(b)	(i)	$I = 35$ mA (from graph) (1) $P = IV$ (1) $(P = 0.035 \times 2.1)$ $P = 0.074$ W (1)		3
		(ii)	Greater number of <u>photons</u> (strike the solar cell) <u>per second</u>		1
15.	(a)		$R = \frac{\rho L}{A}$ $R = \frac{2.8 \times 10^{-8} \times 0.82}{4.0 \times 10^{-6}}$ (1) $R = 5.7 \times 10^{-3} \Omega$ (1)		2
	(b)	(i)	Suitable scales with labels on axes (quantity and unit) (1) [Allow for axes starting at zero or broken axes or starting at an appropriate value] Correct plotting of points (1) Best fit line (1)		3
		(ii)	Choosing 2 points on line drawn (1) Calculate gradient : accept value between 3.7×10^{-3} and 4.0×10^{-3} (Ω m^{-1}) (1) (min 1 sig fig, max 4 sig figs)		2
		(iii)	$\rho = gradient \times A$ (1) $\rho = 3.7 \times 10^{-3} \times 4.52 \times 10^{-6}$ (1) $\rho = 1.7 \times 10^{-8}$ Ωm (1)		3

HIGHER PHYSICS 2018

SECTION 1

Question	Answer	Mark
1.	C	1
2.	D	1
3.	A	1
4.	B	1
5.	A	1
6.	C	1
7.	D	1
8.	B	1
9.	E	1
10.	C	1
11.	B	1
12.	A	1
13.	D	1
14.	D	1
15.	E	1
16.	C	1
17.	D	1
18.	D	1
19.	E	1
20.	C	1

SECTION 2

Question			Answer	Max mark
1.	(a)	(i) (A)	$u_h = 7 \cdot 4 \cos 30$ $u_h = 6 \cdot 4 \text{ m s}^{-1}$ (1) (Accept: 6, 6·41, 6·409)	1
		(i) (B)	$u_v = 7 \cdot 4 \sin 30$ $u_v = 3 \cdot 7 \text{ m s}^{-1}$ (1) (Accept: 4, 3·70, 3·700)	1
		(ii)	$v = u + at$ (1) $0 = 3 \cdot 7 + (-9 \cdot 8)t$ (1) $t = 0 \cdot 38 \text{ s}$ (1) (Accept: 0·4, 0·378, 0·3776)	3
		(iii)	$s = ut + \frac{1}{2}at^2$ (1) $s = (3 \cdot 7 \times 0 \cdot 83) + (0 \cdot 5 \times -9 \cdot 8 \times 0 \cdot 83^2)$ (1) $h = 1 \cdot 5 + \left((3 \cdot 7 \times 0 \cdot 83) \right.$ $\left. \times \left(0 \cdot 5 \times -9 \cdot 8 \times 0 \cdot 83^2 \right) \right)$ (1) $h = 1 \cdot 2 \text{ m}$ (1) (Accept: 1, 1·20, 1·195)	4

Question			Answer	Max mark
	(b)		(Initial) vertical/horizontal speed is greater. (1) Sponge is higher than the teacher when it has travelled the same horizontal distance. OR Sponge has travelled further horizontally when it is at the same height as the teacher. (1)	2
2.	(a)	(i)	$W = mg$ (1) $W = (5 \cdot 50 + 1 \cdot 25) \times 9 \cdot 8$ (1) $W = 66 \text{ N}$ (1) (Accept: 70, 66·2, 66·15)	3
		(ii)	$P = \frac{V^2}{R}$ (1) $P = \frac{12^2}{9 \cdot 6}$ (1) $P = 15 \text{ W}$ (1) (Accept: 20, 15·0, 15·00)	3
		(iii)	Drone accelerates upwards (1) Upward force is greater than weight OR (Upward force remains constant but) weight decreases therefore forces are no longer balanced. OR (Upward force remains constant but) weight decreases therefore there is an unbalanced force (upwards). (1)	2
	(b)		$W = mg$ $W = 3 \cdot 4 \times 9 \cdot 8$ $W = 33 \cdot 32 \text{ (N)}$ (1) Each cord supports $33 \cdot 32/2 = 16 \cdot 66 \text{ (N)}$ (1) $F \cos 35 = 16 \cdot 66$ (1) $F = 20 \text{ N}$ (1) Accept: 20·3, 20·34 Accept: $F \sin 55 = 16 \cdot 66$ $F = 20 \text{ N}$	4
3.	(a)		(Total momentum before = Total momentum after) $p = mv$ OR (1) $(m_x u_x + m_y u_y) = (m_x v_x + m_y v_y)$ $(0 \cdot 75 \times 0 \cdot 50) + (0 \cdot 50 \times -0 \cdot 30)$ $= (0 \cdot 75 \times 0 \cdot 02) + (0 \cdot 50 v_y)$ (1) $v_y = 0 \cdot 42 \text{ m s}^{-1}$	2

Question			Answer	Max mark
	(b)		$Ft = mv - mu$ $\qquad$ (1) $Ft = (0 \cdot 50 \times 0 \cdot 42)$ $\qquad - (0 \cdot 50 \times -0 \cdot 30)$ $\qquad$ (1) $Ft = 0 \cdot 36$ N s $\qquad$ (1) (Accept: 0·4 Accept: Impulse $= mv - mu$ Accept: kg m s^{-1})	3
	(c)		Calculate the total kinetic energy before and (total kinetic energy) after. $\qquad$ (1) If E_k before is equal to E_k after the collision, is elastic. **OR** If E_k before is greater than E_k after, the collision is inelastic. $\qquad$ (1) (Accept: If kinetic energy is not the same, collision is inelastic.)	2
4.			Demonstrates no understanding 0 marks Demonstrates limited understanding 1 mark Demonstrates reasonable understanding 2 marks Demonstrates good understanding 3 marks This is an open-ended question. **1 mark:** The student has demonstrated a limited understanding of the physics involved. The student has made some statement(s) which is/are relevant to the situation, showing that at least a little of the physics within the problem is understood. **2 marks:** The student has demonstrated a reasonable understanding of the physics involved. The student makes some statement(s) which is/are relevant to the situation, showing that the problem is understood.	3

Question			Answer	Max mark
			3 marks: The maximum available mark would be awarded to a student who has demonstrated a good understanding of the physics involved. The student shows a good comprehension of the physics of the situation and has provided a logically correct answer to the question posed. This type of response might include a statement of the principles involved, a relationship or an equation, and the application of these to respond to the problem. This does not mean the answer has to be what might be termed an "excellent" answer or a "complete" one.	
5.	(a)		Cosmic Microwave Background Radiation **OR** Olber's Paradox **OR** Abundance of Hydrogen and Helium in the Universe (Accept: Abundance of Light elements in the Universe)	1
	(b)	(i)	$\left(\text{Age} = \dfrac{1}{H_0} \right)$ $\text{Age} = \dfrac{1}{2 \cdot 0 \times 10^{-17}}$ $\qquad$ (1) $\left(\text{Age} = 5 \cdot 0 \times 10^{16} \, (\text{s}) \right)$ $\qquad$ (1) $\text{Age} = 1 \cdot 6 \times 10^9 \, (\text{years})$ (Accept: 2, 1·58, 1·584 Accept: 2, 1·59, 1·585 if 365 days is used.)	2
	(ii)	(A)	(Student's) value for H_0 is incorrect/too large/not accurate (enough). **OR** Incorrect line (of best fit) drawn. **OR** The (student's) gradient (which is H_0) is too large. **OR** New/more data is available/more accurate. **OR** Not enough data at large distances. (Accept: H_0 varies/decreases as age of the universe increases)	1
		(B)	The student could draw the (correct) line of best fit. **OR** Student could use a larger sample/ all of the 1929 Hubble data. (Accept: The student could use current data.)	1
	(c)		Dark energy	1

Question			Answer	Max mark
6.	(a)	(i)	$W = QV$ (1) $W = 1 \cdot 60 \times 10^{-19} \times 1600$ (1) $W = 2 \cdot 6 \times 10^{-16}\,\text{J}$	2
		(ii)	$E_K = \frac{1}{2}mv^2$ (1) $2 \cdot 6 \times 10^{-16} = \frac{1}{2} \times 9 \cdot 11 \times 10^{-31} \times v^2$ (1) $v = 2 \cdot 4 \times 10^7\,\text{m s}^{-1}$ (1) (Accept: 2, 2·39, 2·389)	3
	(b)		Screen will be brighter/increase glow. (1) Electrons will gain more energy/ move faster. **OR** Increase in number of electrons per second. (1)	2
	(c)		Demonstrates no understanding 0 marks Demonstrates limited understanding 1 mark Demonstrates reasonable understanding 2 marks Demonstrates good understanding 3 marks This is an open-ended question. **1 mark:** The student has demonstrated a limited understanding of the physics involved. The student has made some statement(s) which is/are relevant to the situation, showing that at least a little of the physics within the problem is understood. **2 marks:** The student has demonstrated a reasonable understanding of the physics involved. The student makes some statement(s) which is/are relevant to the situation, showing that the problem is understood.	3

Question			Answer	Max mark
			3 marks: The maximum available mark would be awarded to a student who has demonstrated a good understanding of the physics involved. The student shows a good comprehension of the physics of the situation and has provided a logically correct answer to the question posed. This type of response might include a statement of the principles involved, a relationship or an equation, and the application of these to respond to the problem. This does not mean the answer has to be what might be termed an "excellent" answer or a "complete" one.	
7.	(a)		Frequency of UV/photons/light is not high enough. **OR** Frequency of UV/photons/light is less than threshold frequency. **OR** Energy of photons (of UV light) is not high enough. **OR** Energy of photons (of UV light) is less than work function. **OR** May not be a 'clean plate'.	1
	(b)	(i)	$6 \cdot 94 \times 10^{-19}$ joules of energy is the minimum energy required for (photo) electrons to be emitted/ ejected/photoemission (of electrons).	1
		(ii)	No change (to the kinetic energy). (1) As the irradiance does not affect the energy of the photons/ $E = hf$ is unchanged. (1)	2
	(c)		Lower starting frequency. (1) Same gradient. (1)	2
	(d)		Each photon contains a fixed/ discrete amount of energy. **OR** Each photon removes one electron.	1
8.	(a)	(i)	Waves <u>meet</u> in phase. **OR** Crest <u>meets</u> crest. **OR** Trough <u>meets</u> trough. **OR** Path difference = mλ (Accept: peak for crest.)	1
		(ii)	$m\lambda = d\sin\theta$ (1) $3 \times 630 \times 10^{-9} = \frac{1}{250\,000}\sin\theta$ (1) $\theta = 28°$ (1) (Accept: 30°, 28·2°, 28·20°)	3

Question			Answer	Max mark
		(iii)	Spots will be further apart. **OR** Angle θ is greater. (1) Slit separation d of new grating is smaller than the previous grating. (1)	2
		(iv)	(The waves from the laser have a) constant phase relationship (and have the same frequency, wavelength, and velocity).	1
	(b)		(Polymer) note has vertical and horizontal or crossed lines/grid/grating. (Accept: crosshatch, mesh Accept: diagram to aid description)	1
9.	(a)		$n = \dfrac{\sin\theta_1}{\sin\theta_2}$ (1) $n = \dfrac{\sin 45 \cdot 0}{\sin 22 \cdot 0}$ (1) $n = 1 \cdot 89$ (Accept: $\dfrac{n_2}{n_1} = \dfrac{\sin\theta_1}{\sin\theta_2}$ (1) $\dfrac{n_2}{1} = \dfrac{\sin 45 \cdot 0}{\sin 22 \cdot 0}$ (1) $n = 1 \cdot 89$)	2
	(b)	(i)	The angle of incidence such that the angle of refraction is 90°.	1
		(ii)	$\sin\theta_c = \dfrac{1}{n}$ (1) $\sin\theta_c = \dfrac{1}{1 \cdot 89}$ (1) $\theta_c = 31 \cdot 9°$ (1) (Accept: 32°, 31·94°, 31·945°)	3
		(iii)	 Total Internal Reflection (1) 38° (1) Refraction away from the normal on exit (1) 22° and 45° (1)	4

Question			Answer	Max mark
	(c)		Less deviation in spectrum position. **OR** Less dispersion. (Accept: Spectrum position higher on screen Smaller spread/width of spectrum Brighter spectrum)	1
10.	(a)		A (central) positively charged nucleus. (Negatively charged) electrons in (discrete) energy levels/shells (orbiting the nucleus, not radiating energy.) When an electron moves from one state to another, the energy lost or gained is done so ONLY in very specific amounts of energy. Each line in a spectrum is produced when an electron moves from one energy level/orbit/shell to another.	2
	(b)		$E_2 - E_1 = hf$ (1) $-1 \cdot 36 \times 10^{-19} - (-5 \cdot 45 \times 10^{-19}) = 6 \cdot 63 \times 10^{-34} \times f$ (1) $f = 6 \cdot 17 \times 10^{14}$ Hz (1) (Accept: 6·2, 6·169, 6·1689 Accept: $(\Delta)E = hf$ or $E_3 - E_1 = hf$ for formula mark Accept: $5 \cdot 45 \times 10^{-19} - 1 \cdot 36 \times 10^{-19} = 6 \cdot 63 \times 10^{-34} \times f$ for substitution mark)	3
	(c)		$z = \dfrac{\lambda_o - \lambda_r}{\lambda_r}$ (1) $z = \dfrac{661 - 656}{656}$ (1) $\left(z = 7 \cdot 62195122 \times 10^{-3}\right)$ $z = \dfrac{v}{c}$ (1) $7 \cdot 62195122 \times 10^{-3} = \dfrac{v}{3 \cdot 00 \times 10^8}$ (1) $v = 2 \cdot 29 \times 10^6$ m s^{-1} (1) (Accept: 2·3, 2·287, 2·2866)	5

Question			Answer	Max mark
11.	(a)		The number of joules/energy gained by/supplied to 1 coulomb (of charge passing through the cell).	1
	(b)		Calculate the gradient of the line, for example: $$\text{gradient} = \frac{(290 \times 10^{-3} - 470 \times 10^{-3})}{(105 \times 10^{-6} - 55 \times 10^{-6})} \quad (1)$$ gradient $= -3600$ (1) (gradient $= -r$) $r = 3600\ \Omega$ (1) (Accept: 4000)	3
	(c)		The electrons do not gain enough energy to move into/towards the conduction band of the p-type.	1
12.	(a)	(i)	$(3 \times 1 \cdot 0 =)\ 3 \cdot 0$ V (1) (Accept: 3, 3·00, 3·000)	1
		(ii)	$f = \dfrac{1}{T}$ (1) $f = \dfrac{1}{2}$ (1) $f = 0 \cdot 5$ Hz (1) (Accept: 0·50, 0·500)	3
		(iii)	The LEDs will light when they are forward biased. (1) The change in polarity of voltage changes the biasing. (1)	2
	(b)		$V_2 = \left(\dfrac{R_2}{R_1 + R_2}\right) V_s$ (1) $V_2 = \left(\dfrac{82}{68 + 82}\right) \times 3 \cdot 0$ (1) $V_2 = 1 \cdot 64$ (V) $V_{peak} = \sqrt{2} V_{rms}$ (1) $1 \cdot 64 = \sqrt{2} V_{rms}$ (1) $V_{rms} = 1 \cdot 2$ V (1) (Accept: 1, 1·16, 1·160)	5
13.	(a)		$p = 1 \cdot 00 \times 10^3 \times 9 \cdot 8 \times 0 \cdot 35$ (1) $p = 3 \cdot 4 \times 10^3$ Pa (1) (Accept: 3, 3·43, 3·430)	2
	(b)	(i)	Suitable scales with labels on axes (quantity and units) (1) Correct plotting of points (1) Appropriate line of best fit (1)	3

Question			Answer	Max mark
		(ii)	Calculate the gradient of the line, for example: $$m = \frac{y_2 - y_1}{x_2 - x_1}$$ $$m = \frac{4 \cdot 9 \times 10^3 - 1 \cdot 2 \times 10^3}{0 \cdot 40 - 0 \cdot 10} \quad (1)$$ $= 12\ 000$ (Pa m^{-1}) (1) (Accept: $$m = \frac{y_2 - y_1}{x_2 - x_1}$$ $$m = \frac{4 \cdot 9 - 1 \cdot 2}{0 \cdot 40 - 0 \cdot 10} \quad (1)$$ $= 12$ (kPa m^{-1}) (1)	2
		(iii)	(gradient $= \rho g$) $12\ 000 = \rho g$ (1) $\rho = 1 \cdot 2 \times 10^3$ kg m^{-3} (1)	2

HIGHER PHYSICS
2018 SPECIMEN QUESTION PAPER

PAPER 1

Question	Answer	Max mark
1.	C	1
2.	A	1
3.	B	1
4.	C	1
5.	C	1
6.	C	1
7.	B	1
8.	B	1
9.	C	1
10.	B	1
11.	D	1
12.	D	1
13.	B	1
14.	E	1
15.	D	1
16.	A	1
17.	E	1
18.	C	1
19.	D	1
20.	C	1
21.	E	1
22.	A	1
23.	A	1
24.	E	1
25.	D	1

PAPER 2

Question			Expected response	Max mark
1.	(a)		$v = u + at$ (1) $20 \cdot 0 = 0 + a \times 4 \cdot 0$ (1) $a = 5 \cdot 0 \text{ m s}^{-2}$ (1) (Accept 5, 5·00, 5·000)	3
	(b)		Motorcycle $s = area\ under\ graph$ (1) $s = \frac{1}{2} \times 4 \cdot 0 \times 20 \cdot 0$ (1) car $s = area\ under\ graph$ $s = 4 \cdot 0 \times 15 \cdot 0$ (1) $s_{between} = (4 \cdot 0 \times 15 \cdot 0)$ $\qquad -(\frac{1}{2} \times 4 \cdot 0 \times 20 \cdot 0)$ $s_{between} = 20 \text{ m}$ (1) (Accept 20·0, 20·00)	4
	(c)	(i)	$F = ma$ (1) $F = 290 \times 5 \cdot 0$ (1) $F = F_{Driving} - F_{Friction}$ $(290 \times 5 \cdot 0) = 1800 - F_{Friction}$ (1) $F_{Friction} = 350 \text{ N}$ (1) (Accept 400, 350·0, 350·00)	4
		(ii)	Frictional force /friction/drag/air resistance increases with speed (1) Driving force must be increased to ensure a constant unbalanced force (1)	2
	(d)		 graph curves (gradually, away from velocity axis) after 5 s	1
2.			Estimate of car mass (500 kg < mass < 3000 kg) (1) Estimate of car speed (20 m s^{-1} < speed < 70 m s^{-1}) (1) $E_k = \frac{1}{2}mv^2$ (1) Final answer (1)	4

Question			Expected response	Max mark
3.	(a)	(i)	$v^2 = u^2 + 2as$ (1) $v^2 = 0 + 2 \times 9 \cdot 8 \times 2 \cdot 0$ (1) $v = 6 \cdot 3 \text{ m s}^{-1}$ OR $(m)gh = \frac{1}{2}(m)v^2$ (1) $(42) \times 9 \cdot 8 \times 2 \cdot 0 = \frac{1}{2}(42)v^2$ (1) $v = 6 \cdot 3 \text{ m s}^{-2}$	2
		(ii)	$\Delta p = mv - mu$ (1) $\Delta p = (42 \times (5 \cdot 3)) - (42 \times (-6 \cdot 3))$ (1) $\Delta p = 490 \text{ kg m s}^{-1}$ (1) (Accept 500, 487, 487·2 Accept alternative direction convention.)	3
		(iii)	$Ft = mv - mu$ (1) $F \times 0 \cdot 50 = 490$ (1) $F = 980 \text{ N}$ (1) Accept 1000, 980·0 (Accept 1000, 980·0)	3
	(b)		Tension (in rope) now has a horizontal component (1) Vertical component of tension (in rope) is unchanged (1)	2
4.	(a)		$d = \bar{v}t$ (1) $d = (3 \cdot 00 \times 10^8 \times 0 \cdot 995) \times 2 \cdot 2 \times 10^{-6}$ (1) $d = 660 \text{ m}$	2
	(b)		$t' = \dfrac{t}{\sqrt{1 - \left(\dfrac{v}{c}\right)^2}}$ (1) $t' = \dfrac{2 \cdot 2 \times 10^{-6}}{\sqrt{1 - \left(\dfrac{0 \cdot 995}{1}\right)^2}}$ (1) $t' = 2 \cdot 2 \times 10^{-5} \text{ s}$ (1) (Accept 2, 2·20, 2·203)	3
	(c)		The mean lifetime of the muon is greater for an observer in Earth's frame of reference. OR The mean distance travelled by a muon is shorter in the muon's frame of reference.	1

Question			Expected response	Max mark
5.	(a)	(i)	The galaxy is moving away from Earth. (1) The apparent wavelengths of the lines of the hydrogen spectrum from the galaxy have increased. (1) OR The apparent frequencies of the lines of the hydrogen spectrum from the galaxy are less than the corresponding frequencies from the laboratory source. OR The frequency of the light from the galaxy has shifted towards the red end of the spectrum. OR Observed light from the galaxy shows redshift.	2
		(ii)	$z = \dfrac{(\lambda_{obs} - \lambda_{rest})}{\lambda_{rest}}$ (1) $z = \dfrac{(676 \times 10^{-9} - 656 \times 10^{-9})}{656 \times 10^{-9}}$ (1) $z = \dfrac{v}{c}$ (1) $\dfrac{(676 \times 10^{-9} - 656 \times 10^{-9})}{656 \times 10^{-9}} = \dfrac{v}{3 \cdot 00 \times 10^8}$ (1) $v = 9 \cdot 15 \times 10^6$ m s^{-1} (1) (Accept 9·1, 9·146, 9·1463)	5
	(b)		$v = H_0 d$ (1) $1 \cdot 2 \times 10^7 = 2 \cdot 3 \times 10^{-18} \times d$ (1) $d = 5 \cdot 2 \times 10^{24}$ m (1) (Accept 5, 5·22, 5·217)	3
	(c)		Award 1 mark where the candidate has demonstrated a limited understanding of the physics involved. They make some statement(s) which are relevant to the situation, showing that they have understood at least a little of the physics within the problem. Award 2 marks where the candidate has demonstrated a reasonable understanding of the physics involved. They make some statement(s) which are relevant to the situation, showing that they have understood the problem.	3

Question			Expected response	Max mark
			Award 3 marks where the candidate has demonstrated a good understanding of the physics involved. They show a good comprehension of the physics of the situation and provide a logically correct answer to the question posed. This type of response might include a statement of the principles involved, a relationship or an equation, and the application of these to respond to the problem. The answer does not need to be 'excellent' or 'complete' for the candidate to gain full marks. Award 0 marks where the candidate has not demonstrated an understanding of the physics involved. There is no evidence that they have recognised the area of physics involved, or they have not given any statement of a relevant physics principle. Award this mark also if the candidate merely restates the physics given in the question.	
6.	(a)	(i)	$W = QV$ (1) $W = 1 \cdot 60 \times 10^{-19} \times 3 \cdot 5 \times 10^4$ (1) $W = 5 \cdot 6 \times 10^{-15}$ J	2
		(ii)	E_k at R $E_k = \frac{1}{2}mv^2$ (1) $E_k = 0 \cdot 5 \times 1 \cdot 673 \times 10^{-27} \times (1 \cdot 2 \times 10^6)^2$ (1) E_k at S $E_k = \frac{1}{2}mv^2$ $\left[0 \cdot 5 \times 1 \cdot 673 \times 10^{-27} \times (1 \cdot 2 \times 10^6)^2\right] + 5 \cdot 6 \times 10^{-15} = 0 \cdot 5 \times 1 \cdot 673 \times 10^{-27} \times v^2$ addition (1) substitution (1) $v = 2 \cdot 9 \times 10^6$ ms^{-1} (1) (Accept 3, 2·85, 2·852)	5
	(b)	(i)	To ensure the (accelerating) force is in the same direction. OR To ensure the protons accelerate in the same direction. OR To ensure that the direction of the electric field is correct when the proton passes through a tube.	1

Question			Expected response	Max mark
		(ii)	Alternating voltage has a constant frequency (rather than a frequency which changes). **OR** As speed of proton increases, they travel further in the same time.	1
	(c)		Downwards	1
7.	(a)		Fundamental particles cannot be subdivided	1
	(b)		$-\dfrac{1}{3}e$	1
	(c)		The strong force (associated with the gluon) has a short range. (1) The gravitational force (requires a force mediating particle which) has infinite range. (1)	2
	(d)		(The strong force is) 13 (orders of magnitude) greater (than the weak force)	1
	(e)		Beta decay	1
8.	(a)		mass loss $m = (4 \times 1\cdot673 \times 10^{-27})$ $\qquad - 6\cdot646 \times 10^{-27}$ (1) $E = mc^2$ (1) $E = ((4 \times 1\cdot673 \times 10^{-27})$ $\qquad - (6\cdot646 \times 10^{-27})) \times (3\cdot00 \times 10^8)^2$ (1) $E = 4\cdot14 \times 10^{-12}$ J (1) (Accept 4·1, 4·140, 4·1400)	4
	(b)		0·20 kg hydrogen has $\dfrac{0\cdot20}{1\cdot673 \times 10^{-27}}\ (= 1\cdot195 \times 10^{26}\,\text{atoms})$ (1) provides $\dfrac{1\cdot195 \times 10^{26}}{4} = 0\cdot2989 \times 10^{26}$ $\qquad\qquad\qquad\qquad$ reactions (1) releases $0\cdot2989 \times 10^{26} \times 4\cdot14 \times 10^{-12}$ $= 1\cdot2 \times 10^{14}$ J (1) (Accept 1, 1·24, 1·237)	3
	(c)		The particles involved in fusion reactions must be at a high temperature	1
9.	(a)		Irradiance is the power incident per unit area	1

Question			Expected response	Max mark
	(b)		Graphical method Correct quantities on axes (I and $1/d^2$) (1) Accuracy of plotting and line of best fit (1) Statement of relationship (1) Do not award statement mark if less than three points plotted accurately.	3
	(c)		(Black cloth) prevents reflections	1
	(d)		The laser is not a point source OR Light from the laser does not conform to the inverse square law OR Laser beam does not spread out	1
10.	(a)	(i)	$v = f\lambda$ (1) $3\cdot00 \times 10^8 = f \times 525 \times 10^{-9}$ (1) $E = hf$ (1) $E = 6\cdot63 \times 10^{-34} \times \left(\dfrac{3\cdot00 \times 10^8}{525 \times 10^{-9}}\right)$ (1) $E = 3\cdot79 \times 10^{-19}$ J	4
		(ii)	$(E_k = 3\cdot79 \times 10^{-19} - 2\cdot24 \times 10^{-19})$ $E_k = 1\cdot55 \times 10^{-19}$ J	1
	(b)	(i)	Photons with frequency below f_0 do not have enough energy to release electrons	1
		(ii)	$E = hf_0$ (1) $2\cdot24 \times 10^{-19} = (6\cdot63 \times 10^{-34}) \times f_0$ (1) $f_0 = 3\cdot38 \times 10^{14}$ Hz (1) (Accept 3·4, 3·379, 3·3786)	3
	(c)		**Award 1 mark** where the candidate has demonstrated a limited understanding of the physics involved. They make some statement(s) which are relevant to the situation, showing that they have understood at least a little of the physics within the problem. **Award 2 marks** where the candidate has demonstrated a reasonable understanding of the physics involved. They make some statement(s) which are relevant to the situation, showing that they have understood the problem.	3

Question			Expected response	Max mark
			Award 3 marks where the candidate has demonstrated a good understanding of the physics involved. They show a good comprehension of the physics of the situation and provide a logically correct answer to the question posed. This type of response might include a statement of the principles involved, a relationship or an equation, and the application of these to respond to the problem. The answer does not need to be 'excellent' or 'complete' for the candidate to gain full marks.	
			Award 0 marks where the candidate has not demonstrated an understanding of the physics involved. There is no evidence that they have recognised the area of physics involved, or they have not given any statement of a relevant physics principle. Award this mark also if the candidate merely restates the physics given in the question.	
11.	(a)		Bright fringes are produced by waves meeting in phase/crest to crest/trough to trough	1
	(b)	(i)	$\Delta x = \dfrac{\lambda D}{d}$ $\dfrac{9 \cdot 5 \times 10^{-3}}{4} = \dfrac{633 \times 10^{-9} \times 0 \cdot 750}{d}$ division by 4 (1) substitutions (1) $d = 2 \cdot 0 \times 10^{-4}$ m (1) (Accept 2, 2·00, 1·999)	3
		(ii)	$\%uncertainty\,\Delta x = \dfrac{0 \cdot 2 \times 10^{-3} \times 100}{9 \cdot 5 \times 10^{-3}}$ $= 2 \cdot 1\%$ (1) $\%uncertainty\,D = \dfrac{0 \cdot 001 \times 100}{0 \cdot 750}$ $= 0 \cdot 13\%$ (1) Improve precision in measurement of Δx (1)	3
	(c)		Green light has a shorter wavelength (1) Fringes are closer together (1)	2
12.	(a)		$n = \dfrac{\sin\theta_1}{\sin\theta_2}$ (1) $n = \dfrac{\sin(51 \cdot 4)}{\sin(36 \cdot 0)}$ (1) $n = 1 \cdot 33$	2

Question			Expected response	Max mark
	(b)	(i)	(Critical angle is) the angle of incidence which produces an angle of refraction of 90°	1
		(ii)	$\sin\theta_c = \dfrac{1}{n}$ (1) $\sin\theta_c = \dfrac{1}{1 \cdot 33}$ (1) $\theta_c = 48 \cdot 8°$ (1) (Accept 49, 48·75, 48·753)	3
13.	(a)	(i)	2·5 Ω	1
		(ii)	$E = \dfrac{y_2 - y_1}{x_2 - x_1}$ $E = \dfrac{11 - 0}{0 \cdot 80 - 0 \cdot 15}$ substitution of two points on line (1) $E = 17$ V (1)	2
	(b)		$V = IR$ (1) $17 = I \times 2 \cdot 5$ (1) $I = 6 \cdot 8$ A (1)	3
14.	(a)		$V = IR$ (1) $12 = 3 \cdot 0 \times 10^{-5} \times R$ (1) $R = 4 \cdot 0 \times 10^{5}$ Ω (1) (Accept 4, 4·00, 4·000)	3
	(b)	(i)	$Q = It$ (1) $Q = 3 \cdot 0 \times 10^{-5} \times 25$ (1) $Q = 7 \cdot 5 \times 10^{-4}$ C (1) (Accept: 8, 7·50, 7·500)	3
		(ii)	$C = \dfrac{Q}{V}$ (1) $220 \times 10^{-6} = \dfrac{7 \cdot 5 \times 10^{-4}}{V}$ (1) $V = 3 \cdot 4$ (V) (1) Therefore voltage across resistor is $12 - 3 \cdot 4 = 8 \cdot 6$ V (1) (Accept 9, 8·59, 8·591)	4
15.	(a)		Material 2	1
	(b)		(Voltage applied causes) electrons to move towards conduction band of p-type (1) Electrons move/drop from conduction band to valence band (1) Photon emitted (when electron drops) (1)	3

Question			Expected response	Max mark
16.	(a)		Suitable scales with labels on axes (quantity and unit) (1) Points plotted accurately (1) Acceptable line(curve) of best fit (1)	3
	(b)		7·5 mm ±1mm	1
	(c)		Repeat measurements (1) Smaller steps/divisions/intervals in radius (around the 75% value or equivalent) (1)	2

Acknowledgements

Permission has been sought from all relevant copyright holders and Hodder Gibson is grateful for the use of the following:

Image © KieferPix/stock.adobe.com (2017 Section 2 page 6);
Image © Flik47/Shutterstock.com (2017 Section 2 page 12);
Image © Snap2Art/Shutterstock.com (2018 Section 2 page 6);
Image © Studio Caramel/Shutterstock.com (2018 Section 2 page 10);
Image © Jason Allemann (http://jkbrickworks.com) (2018 Section 2 page 20);
Image © Daseaford/Shutterstock.com (2018 SQP Section 2 page 24).